The Grosvenor House Antiques Fair

10th–20th June 1987

Presented by
Trusthouse Forte PLC

in association with
The British Antique Dealers' Association

and organised by
Evan Steadman and Partners Limited

1987 HANDBOOK

Published in association with The Antique Collector magazine

Opening times for the Fair

The Fair will be open every day at the following
times:

10th June: 5.00 p.m. to 8.00 p.m.

11th, 12th, 15th, 16th, 17th, 18th and 19th June:
11.00 a.m. to 8.00 p.m.

13th, 14th and 20th June: 11.00 a.m. to 6.00 p.m.

Visitors and Exhibitors are reminded that, in
accordance with Westminster City Council
regulations, money may not change hands on Sunday.

Organised by Evan Steadman and Partners Limited
from The Hub, Emson Close, Saffron Walden,
Essex CB10 1HL, United Kingdom.
Telephone (0799) 26699
Telex 81653 INFORM G Fax (0799) 26088

© National Magazine Company Ltd. 1987

Handbook edited, produced and designed by
The Antique Collector: Isabel Boucher, Alan Boxall,
Ed Cadman.
Printed by Balding + Mansell UK Limited,
London and Wisbech

Acknowledgements

The Organisers of the 1987 Grosvenor House
Antiques Fair wish to thank the following for their
invaluable assistance and co-operation.

The Fair Committee

The Vetting Committees

Garrard & Company Limited for kindly allowing the
use of the magnificent Paul Storr Candelabrum for
promotional purposes.

Thanks are also due to the Royal School of
Needlework for their support and co-operation in
providing outstanding loan displays; and to the Royal
School and MENCAP for their association with the
Charity Preview.

We also acknowledge the contribution to the
screening of the Purple Velvet Coronation Robe by
Rivermeade Signs Limited.

We are indebted to both Janet Turner, Fair Lighting
Consultant, and Richard Daniels, Fair Design
Consultant, for their expertise and guidance in further
enhancing the most prestigious Fair in the world.

Our thanks are also extended to ten of the country's
major fabric houses: G.P. & J. Baker Limited; Nina
Campbell Limited; Jane Churchill Design Limited;
Decorator Collection – Laura Ashley Limited;
Osborne and Little plc; Pallu & Lake; Michael Szell
Limited; Textra Limited; Bernard Thorp; and
Warner & Sons Limited, who very kindly worked
alongside ten of our participants to create specially
designed and fashioned displays.

Finally we would like to thank David Pettifer,
President of The British Antique Dealers'
Association, for his many contributions as
Co-Chairman of the Fair and whose term of office
ends as the Fair closes. We look forward to welcoming
his successor.

Title page photograph
The Artefact of The Year at The 1986 Fair.

An important George III silver-gilt centrepiece by the Royal Goldsmith, Paul Storr, surmounted by the cast seated figure of
Peace supported on a thick foliate stem with three cast branches. The whole resting on a triangular base, the upper part
engraved on one side with the crest and cartouche of the original owner, Thomas Maitland, the second side with a moulded
frieze of Ceylon elephants, the third side an engraved presentation and testimonial to Thomas Maitland, the beneficiary. Dated 1814.
Overall height: 88 cm (34½ in) Area of base: 52 cm (20½ in) Span of branches: 53 cm (21 in) Weight: 849.5 ozs.
Courtesy: Garrard & Company Limited (The Crown Jewellers) *Photograph:* Prudence Cuming Associates

Opening Ceremony

Their Majesties
King Constantine and Queen Anne-Marie of The Hellenes

The Grosvenor House Antiques Fair

The Fair Committee

Christopher Clarke
Paul Clarke
Elaine Dean
Francis Green
Jonathan Harris
Brand Inglis
Roger Keverne
George Lehrian
Penny Marks
Baden Marston
Brian Morgan
Nicolas Norton
David Pettifer (Co-Chairman)
Olga Polizzi (Co-Chairman)
Alistair Sampson
Evan Steadman
Alison Vaissière

The Vetting Committees

Arms & Armour
Reginald Gwynn
Geoffrey Jenkinson
Howard Ricketts

Books & Manuscripts
Thomas Heneage
John Maggs
Martin Orskey

Carpets, Rugs & Textiles
Simon Franses
Mansour Heskia
Alexander Juran
Natalie Rothstein
Lanto Synge
Antoine de Vermoutier

Clocks, Watches, Barometers & Scientific Instruments
David Bryden
Simon Bull
John de Haan
Beresford Hutchinson
Charles Lee
Ronald A. Lee
Daniel Parkes
Jack Pearce
Harriet Wynter

European Ceramics
Kate Foster
Michael Graham
Jonathan Horne
Robert Jones
Betty Klaber
Pamela Klaber
Stafford Lorie
Emily Manheim
Pearl Manheim
Alistair Sampson
Mary Wise

European Sculpture, Works of Art & Antiquities
Jonathan Harris
John Hewett
Thomas Howard-Sneyd
Alastair Laing
Ronald A. Lee
Howard Ricketts
Elizabeth Wilson

Furniture & Architectural Items
Bernard Apter
Terry Baxter
Peter Cheek
Christopher Clarke
Richard Courtney
Thomas Crispin
Nicholas Fowle
Jonathan Harris
Ian Hastie
John Hill
Michael Hill
Tobias Jellinek
Andrew Jenkins
John Keil
Robin Kern
Charles Lee
Baden Marston
David Nickerson
David Pettifer
Henry Rubin
Jacob Stodel
Stewart Whittington

Glass
Derek Davis
Ward Lloyd
Maureen Thompson

Glass Pictures, Tôle & Papier Mâché
Paul Clarke
Martin Levy
Lanto Synge

Icons
Maria Andipa
Yanni Petsopoulos

Jewellery, Bijouterie, Snuff Boxes, Miniatures & Enamels
Susan Benjamin
Shirley Bury
Walter Hakim
David Lavender
Brian Norman
Jonathan Norton
Martin Norton

Metalwork
Christopher Bangs
James Brett
Michael Casimir
Peter Hornsby
Richard Mundey

Numismatics
Richard Falkiner

Oriental Ceramics & Works of Art
Richard Barker
Anthony Carter
Paul Champkins
David Freedman
Michael Gillingham
Gerard Hawthorn
Roger Keverne
Richard Marchant
Brian Morgan
Paul Moss

Ormolu
John Hill
David Nickerson
Henry Rubin
Jacob Stodel

Paintings, Drawings & Prints
Timothy Bathurst
Christopher Bibby
William Darby
Evert Douwes
William Drummond
David Fuller
John Hayes
Peter Mitchell
David Posnett
John Sabin
Anthony Speelman
Anthony Spink
Rafael Valls
Johnny Van Haeften
Christopher Wood

Silver & Sheffield Plate
Philippa Glanville
Brand Inglis
Edmund Laird Clowes
Nicolas Norton
Charles Shrubsole
Hugh Tait

Treen & Bygones
Thomas Crispin
Anthony Foster
Michael Gillingham
Andrew Jenkins
Baden Marston

Contents

The Importance of Vetting

A new collector can always buy at The Grosvenor House Antiques Fair with complete confidence. Appealing to many interests there is, overall, a wide and carefully maintained balance of exhibitors. The very high standard of the items shown and for sale is ensured by 'vetting'. This is the system whereby an independent group of experts examines and assesses every item at the Fair before it is allowed to be shown to the public.

There are 18 vetting committees, each with a different speciality. The members, some 125 people in all, comprise academics, auctioneers and dealers (some of whom are exhibitors). When the stock on any particular stand is being examined neither the exhibitor nor a representative can be present. This ensures impartiality and the opportunity for the members of the vetting committee to express their views freely.

The stringency of the vetting procedures is one form of guarantee of the quality and the genuineness of all the items on display and for sale at The Grosvenor House Antiques Fair. Such concerns are essentially a matter of opinion, which is why they are settled independently by the vetting committee members, each of whom is recognised as expert in a particular field. They are keen to maintain their own individual reputations and to uphold the reputation of the Fair as a whole.

The following points constitute a series of basic criteria which must be fulfilled before an item can be considered for inclusion at the Fair.

1. It must be a genuine antique or work of art of the period that it is represented to be.
2. It must have been made before or during 1887. Pictures, bronzes, sculpture, book bindings and manuscripts will be accepted if made before or during 1914. Works of art of later periods than these may be admitted to the Fair at the discretion of the appropriate committee, provided they are of sufficient importance.
3. The item must be in its original form and not over restored.
4. It must be properly attributed and correctly labelled giving a brief description and the date it was made.
5. It must be of such a standard and in such a condition that its inclusion is not contrary to the best interests of the Fair as a whole.

6. Apart from exhibits included in any Loan Display, the item must be for sale.

With the passing of years it is inevitable that there will be a change in the appearance of many items. For example, both antique furniture and antique silver can acquire a 'patina' that is an essential part of their character and attraction today. Furthermore, in the course of time and use, many items will sustain wear or damage. Thus some forms of restoration are permitted at the Fair. Once again there are strict guidelines for the vetting committee.

1. Regilding or repainting of furniture is acceptable if it does not exclude evidence of antiquity.
2. With cabinets and desks, missing or damaged feet or plinths may be replaced if they are of the same character as the original.
3. For looking glasses, a missing mirror plate or central surmounting feature may be replaced.
4. In the case of tables, missing marble tops, or missing loose leaves from 18th- and 19th-century dining tables may be replaced.
5. With regard to clocks, worn parts including hands may be replaced by those of the same character as the original.

Sometimes substitution may be permitted under the terms, once again, of strict guidelines.

1. Leather may be replaced on table tops if the value of the item is not thereby increased.
2. Elaborate modern frames may be provided for Chinese mirror pictures.
3. For chairs made in and after 1775, upholstery may be substituted for cane seats, provided the backs were not caned originally.
4. With clocks, a verge escapement may be replaced by a later form.
5. Clocks with decorative cases, ranking as works of art in their own right and for which the movements are incidental, may have later or modern movements.

Reductions are allowed only in the cases of prints or maps with trimmed top and side margins.

Under no circumstances will the vetting committees ever permit examples of the following to be exhibited at the Fair.

1. Any item that has been so restored as to exclude evidence of serious or extensive damage.
2. Marriages of any kind: that is items made of two or more individual sections each of which originally formed part of other, different items.
3. Any item with additions, subtractions, later enrichments, or any alterations that change its original character or enhance its value.

In the best interests of the Fair as a whole, the vetting committees are also empowered to exclude exhibits of the following kinds:

1. Sideboards or tables which have been reduced in depth or in size generally.
2. Plain items which have been carved, inlaid or cross-banded at a later date.
3. Mirrors with original designs that have been altered, or with decorated glass borders or panels that are not as the original.
4. Gilt gesso tables with new gesso tops.
5. Furniture with a solid plinth altered to bracket feet or with bracket feet replaced by a plinth.
6. Blind, wooden doors altered to take glass or wirecage.
7. Painted furniture repainted with embellishments or a change of colour.
8. Settees (and chairs) made before 1775 which originally had cane seats but are now upholstered.
9. Clocks in which the original movements have been entirely replaced, save where these are wholly incidental to items with a decorative case.
10. Prints or maps in which the pictorial surface has been reduced, or has modern colouring.

These are complicated matters, even for experts. Therefore to help visitors to The Grosvenor House Antiques Fair every exhibit, with the exception of small items of jewellery, has a descriptive label. Each label is examined by the vetting committee, which insists that the details are comprehensive and accurate and accord with the committee members' own opinion. So for example, if the dealer owning the item maintains that it is of a particular date not acceptable to the vetting committee, then the label must be changed or the item removed from the Fair. Where relevant, the label must also contain other helpful information.

1. An item made at a later period than suggested by its general style must be labelled to indicate its approximate date.
2. An item which appears to be of British origin but is not must be labelled with its country of origin or with the words 'continental' or 'foreign'.
3. Paintings, drawings and prints must be labelled to include the name of the artist with his or her dates or the date of the item. If unknown then the school or approximate date must be stated.

These stringent safeguards ensure that all items for sale at The Grosvenor House Antiques Fair not only maintain the high standards that are the hallmarks of this famous Fair, but are accurately described to the best knowledge of the independent expert members of the vetting committees. Stock is replenished on a daily basis throughout the course of the Fair and each fresh item is subject to the same rigorous procedures we have outlined above.

David Pettifer
PRESIDENT, British Antique Dealers' Association;
Co-Chairman, The Grosvenor House Antiques Fair.

Christopher Clarke
CHAIRMAN, The Grosvenor House Antiques Fair Vetting Committees.

Chinese Art for Collectors

by Michael Gillingham

Chinese art is remarkable for its enormous time-span and great range of materials. That it has long been appreciated in the West is shown by documented pieces such as the Chinese celadon-glazed pots mounted in silver in the Middle Ages, the 16th- and 17th-century blue-and-white porcelain (some set in Elizabethan silver) at Burghley House, the collections at royal residences such as Hampton Court and the Chinese Pavilion at Drottningholm.

Classical fields of collecting included magnificent archaic bronzes from the Shang and Zhou periods (1600–221 BC) which were revealed by excavations and brought to the West in the early part of this century. The discovery of the tomb potteries — the horses, camels and other figures of the Tang dynasty (618–907) — opened Western eyes to something vivid: chestnut-yellow and green glazes had an immediate decorative appeal. In the 1930s every grand house had to have a Tang horse on the grand piano along with the signed photographs.

Another, more academic, area of collecting popular during the 1930s was Song ceramics. This extraordinarily sophisticated porcelain with its exquisite colours and simple shapes had a pure aesthetic appeal, producing a unique response in people's minds. It does not give the baroque sensation of drapery in a Rubens painting, it is an appeal to one's appreciation of restraint in line and colour.

The later periods, the Ming and Qing dynasties (1368–1911), offer objects with more lavish decoration and with pictorial elements where plain colours sufficed before. There was great skill in arranging formal decoration on the restricted shapes of porcelain pieces, and in painting freehand on to a difficult medium where there could be no corrections. The colours that were thus preserved beneath the glaze do give an absolutely accurate and vivid idea of the colour palette then available. In Chinese porcelain we see the unfaded hues of the 18th century.

From the 17th century onwards, there were artefacts made especially for export to the West. These include porcelain copying western shapes and curiously translating western decorative styles, Chinese mirror paintings, and reverse paintings on glass which are often found with contemporary western gilt rococo frames. Since the last war there has been a tremendous growth of interest in Chinese export art in America, a country which did much trade with China in the 18th century.

Amongst the factors that have affected the market recently one or two may be mentioned. Prices of the finest Chinese porcelains have rocketed due to the presence in the market of rich and discriminating collectors from Japan, Hong Kong and Singapore. The best Song and Ming porcelain is now well beyond the reach of any but the richest collectors. There is still, however, potential for collecting at a more realistic level in what used patronisingly to be called 'the minor arts': jade, lacquer, carved hardstone, textiles, ivory and organic materials. Interest in these has quickened and modern taste especially favours the simple and subtle objects made traditionally for the Scholar's Table. This trend away from large ornate pieces reflects changes in styles of living. The luxurious objects that appealed to the 'international grand taste' of the 1920s and 1930s now tend to find homes in middle eastern collections.

Another influence in the market is the interest in interior decoration which has developed in the last thirty to forty years. The 'English Country House' style which has been promoted in America focused attention on 17th- and 18th-century decorative porcelains. It also lent a certain respectability to damaged porcelain; the most perspicacious decorators understand that a few 18th-century rivets holding a decorative vase together add a touch of authentic country-house history.

There are still areas in which there is much yet to be discovered and plenty of fun to be had. For example, bronzes of the Song and Ming periods are historically interesting, and examples can be found which have good sculptural qualities and a certain presence. These may be purchased from £500 upwards, which is not an extravagant way to begin. Then the collector will learn a little more, and his next purchase will be a little older and a little better.

These days collectors must be well informed and have an eye for quality. The Grosvenor House Antiques Fair offers a unique opportunity for collectors to see the best that is available, to discuss and to learn in an encouraging and good-natured environment and to establish a mutually profitable contact with experts in the field.

A pair of 18th-century Chinese figures,
probably portraits of a Mandarin and his wife,
in mixed media. Lacquer, ivory, textile and painted plaster
are used to give a most life-like effect.
Examples of such figures,
including portraits of European merchants,
can be found in many European collections.

English Silver for Collectors

by Edmund Laird Clowes

A taste for quality dominates the antique silver market and has led to astronomic prices being paid for important pieces. In the past good ordinary silver sold well at Grosvenor House but dealers now offer fewer pieces, each of a very high standard. This means, sadly, that the enthusiastic collector with £1000–£1500 to spend has almost disappeared. Although the dealer does not promote it, investment undoubtedly plays a part in today's market. With five- or six-figure sums involved it is too much to expect the purchaser not to have at least a weather-eye on the continuing value of his money. While some buyers lock their silver away in bank vaults as safe investments, others buy primarily for their own aesthetic pleasure.

It is difficult to pinpoint a period that finds particular favour in the market but I believe there will always be collectors for the finest and rarest pieces of all periods. As keenly sought as ever is the work by the great Huguenot silversmith, Paul de Lamerie. His reputation is well deserved for he had a remarkable gift and his finest pieces have a touch of magic which sets them apart. The record-breaking prices such pieces command reflect this, and I must mention in passing Lamerie's magnificent centre-piece which sold for £770,000 late last year at Christie's, his silver kettle on stand at $187,000 and his pair of figure candlesticks at £275,000. Comparable silversmiths of this period include Philip Rollos and David Willaume (fathers and sons), Paul Crespin and Peter Archambo, all of whom made marvellous things.

There is also a healthy interest in the best examples of 19th-century silver and Paul Storr is still the leading name. Visitors to this Fair last year will remember the exceptional candelabrum which he made and which won the Artefact of the Year Award. In this context one should also mention Philip Rundell, Benjamin Smith and Robert Garrard. Curiously enough there is little demand for the work of the late 18th-century silversmith, Hester Bateman, who was so keenly collected by Americans some years ago, but this is no doubt partly due to the deaths of three enthusiastic collectors. It is also due to the fact that her work seldom, if ever, displayed really fine workmanship. The same applies to the run of neo-classical silver which was made in large quantities in the last thirty years of the 18th century. A few exceptional pieces command high prices, as do good services of spoons and forks which are becoming rarer.

As the interest in ordinary domestic silver has diminished so have the routine sales which used to figure largely in the dealer's life. Today highly important sales occur two or three times a year and receive enormous advance publicity all over the world and extremely sophisticated 'orchestration' on the day of the sale. Fine English silver has an international appeal and large collections exist worldwide; indeed it was James I who gave one of the most important collections to what is now the Soviet Union. There are avid collectors in nearly all the European countries as well as in America and Canada, in Australia and New Zealand and, as always, in England.

Before concluding I should perhaps say a word about cleaning silver as there is a tendency to over-clean. In order to preserve its colour and 'wear' silver should be kept clean (but not sparkling), rather than waiting until it becomes badly tarnished and then subjecting it to intensive cleaning. Often it is enough simply to wash it in soap and hot water and, after drying it, polish it gently with a chamois leather. As important as colour and wear are the hall-marks which tell one who made a particular piece of silver, in what year and in what town. At all costs the clarity of the hall-marks must be preserved.

This article is an attempt to assess the present market conditions of short supply and strong demand. With this in mind a visit to The Grosvenor House Antiques Fair can be compared with a visit to one of our great historic houses or museums, but with the advantage of being able to buy. With all the Fair's exhibits so carefully vetted, the buyer has every reason to feel confidence in his purchase. This unique Fair is widely regarded by dealers and collectors as the focal point of their year.

George II silver epergne by Paul de Lamerie,
engraved with the arms of Coote impaling Newport.
1736–37.
Height 35.6 cm (14¼ in).
Sold at Christie's on 17th December 1986, lot 240, for £770,000.

English Furniture for Collectors

by Baden Marston

Five years ago when the Fair resumed, good quality furniture was not easy to find in any quantity, and today it is scarcer still. Bearing this in mind the show put on by the dealers at The Grosvenor House Antiques Fair is pretty amazing. This is, in effect, the finest collection of furniture for sale at one time anywhere and it is only achieved by dealers hoarding choice items throughout the year.

The constantly diminishing supply of good furniture, especially the really fine pieces, means that dealers, while never known to be unhappy to sell, are anxious to replace their stock without lowering their standards. This anxiety is, however, almost as old as the furniture. In forty years in the business I cannot remember a time when dealers were not sighing about the difficulty of finding really good pieces, and records suggest this was even lamented in the 18th century.

The effect of short supply and great demand on the antique furniture market has been that later pieces have acquired respectability and even become fashionable. In response to this, the dateline for furniture at this fair was changed in 1983 from the traditional 1830 to the hundred-year-old limit. Fearing an influx of run-of-the-mill Victoriana, I have to say I was unhappy about this change, but have since been pleasantly surprised by the excellent standards that have been maintained. This is no doubt due, in part at least, to the vigilance of the vetting committees whose activities are described elsewhere in these pages.

Good and especially fine pieces of furniture made throughout the 18th and early 19th centuries are still the most sought after, making by far the highest prices. The Americans are enthusiastic buyers in this field, though their absence from these radio-active shores last year can hardly be said to have had much of a depressant effect on prices. Regency furniture, which was not highly regarded by the old school of dealers in the 1930s and 40s, now fetches high prices and is fashionable. Early oak furniture, on the other hand, is not in such demand as it was perhaps four or five years ago. This is mainly due to the lack of Continental buyers who previously bought oak in quantity from this country but are currently less active. Really good oak pieces are still in demand and continue to make the high prices they have since the late 1920s and early 1930s when oak was particularly fashionable.

Regarding English furniture, we have witnessed an enormous increase in prices over the last five years or so, though this pertains especially to really fine pieces. Only a fool would claim to predict the future of the antiques market, but I shall stick my neck out boldly and say that, in my opinion, good English furniture will continue not to come down in price. This forthright opinion is based on the observation that this market is controlled by supply and demand, and there is no doubt which is the larger. Unfortunately for the English collector, and indeed the country, American and some Continental buyers continue to like our furniture, and the truth is that once exported, little of it comes back. To balance this picture, I must say that fine French and American furniture has also made extremely high and record prices during 1986, but perhaps not so consistently as good English furniture.

I am occasionally asked advice about buying antique furniture and my reply has always been the same. The three things to look for are quality, condition and colour, with a good patination if possible. Patina is something that is much misunderstood. To put it plainly, it is accumulated dirt and dust, combined with exposure to light, that age has transformed into that marvellous warm glow seen on the best antique furniture. It is easily ruined by abrasive treatment in the name of 'cleaning' or 'polishing' and deserves the greatest respect. It is especially important to the value of early oak and walnut furniture.

Other factors affecting the price include size. Generally speaking small is expensive, though there are exceptions including large dining tables, long sets of chairs and some mirrors. A bureau 2 ft. 6 in. wide will cost considerably more than a similar quality one say 4 ft. 6 in. wide. Proven provenance or pedigree also enhances value. A good example of this was provided by a pair of George III giltwood side tables sold last year for £286,000 for which documentation included Robert Adam's designs and original invoices for the work. This is especially valuable with English furniture, since unlike French equivalents it is very rarely marked. All these factors have a bearing on value, whether of a highly sophisticated item or a country piece of furniture.

I have always advocated buying the best of its kind that you can afford. I have never encouraged buying antique furniture for investment, although it is true that in retrospect many purchases do turn out to have a wonderful golden lining. Antique furniture should be purchased to use and enjoy and I hope you will get as much pleasure out of it as I have.

An extremely rare Chippendale period carved mahogany chair with original tapestry covering. Circa 1760.
Height of back 106 cm (41½ in).

The Royal School of Needlework

by Lanto Synge

The School of Art Needlework, later known as the Royal School of Needlework, was founded in London in 1872. This was in the wake of a renaissance of artistic design and a new interest in worthwhile craftsmanship; William Morris and his followers had already initiated a revival in creative embroidery, based on a return to the best methods and highest standards of previous periods. Under the presidency of Queen Victoria's daughter, Princess Christian of Schleswig-Holstein, its purpose was 'to supply suitable employment for poor gentlefolk', both in the restoration of old needlework and the creation of new. The committee consisted of distinguished and high-minded ladies such as Lady Marion Alford whose book, *Needlework as Art* (1866), epitomized the serious approach to the subject. The school employed over a hundred women and undertook commissions, working to designs by leading painters including Edward Burne-Jones, William Morris, Lord Leighton and Walter Crane. Prepared works were supplied for ladies to complete in their own homes and the provision of set pieces soon became a substantial business and source of income. An 1880 advertisement for these indicates the practical nature of the pieces chosen for art needlework. Hangings, bedcovers, curtains, screens, tablecloths, cushions, chair-back covers and all sorts of borders were advocated, but the school also listed designs and materials for more curious accessories:

> Tennis Aprons, Folding Screens, Kettledrum D'Oyleys, Photograph Frames, Bellows, Opera Cloaks, Piano Panels, Babies' Head Flannels, Knitting Pockets.

The Royal School of Needlework, however, persisted in its serious aims and in giving training and employment to the 'penurious women of gentle birth'. It encouraged high standards of workmanship, as intended by its founders. The quality of work produced was carefully checked and the school's success led to the formation of other needlework societies, such as the Decorative Needlework Society, The Ladies' Work Society and, among smaller organisations, the Wemyss Castle School in Scotland.

By the end of the century the Royal School was generally esteemed as a national institution, holding extensive exhibitions and with a wide influence in Britain and also to some extent in the United States of America. The start of a new building for it in 1899 was celebrated as something of a minor state occasion. The Prince of Wales laid the foundation stone, the Life Guards paraded, the Royal College of Music performed and the Bishop of London offered a prayer before a rendering of The Old Hundreth. That building was in Exhibition Road, Kensington. Later, the Royal School moved to a nearby site in Prince's Gate, where it has been for many years. It has continued to enjoy royal patronage and has had a tradition of undertaking such important commissions as the making and embroidery of coronation robes, including the one for HM Queen Elizabeth II. Otherwise the most significant work made by the Royal School in modern times must be the Overlord Embroidery, commissioned by Lord Dulverton as a permanent memorial and record of the effort made by the allies to liberate occupied Europe during the Second World War. This colossal frieze of appliqué and embroidery is now exhibited in Portsmouth.

The Royal School of Needlework is also pleased to undertake commissions to make smaller items such as chair seats, or to provide help in the design of any embroidery including personal heraldic needlework, samplers, pictures etc. They will gladly advise on technical matters, preparatory painting of canvas and the supply of wools, cottons and silks, together with any necessary equipment. The School has a shop which provides such articles together with all the other necessaries and pattern books and reference books. It is also pleased to undertake restoration of most forms of textiles, especially needlework and tapestries, even of a large scale. It will also attend to samplers and small items that are in need of cleaning and repair. Careful distinction is made between conservation and restoration according to whichever is desirable in the circumstances. Its other special feature is the programme of teaching classes in which a broad spectrum of techniques may be learned.

It is not generally known that The Royal School of Needlework offers all these services and it would welcome more commissions and restoration work, to be done on a competitive basis and to a standard of the highest quality. Enquiries with regard to obtaining advice or estimates should be addressed to representatives at The Grosvenor House Antique Dealers Fair or to:

The Principal, The Royal School of Needlework,
25 Prince's Gate, London SW7 1QE
Tel: 01-589 0077

Purple Velvet Train designed and worked at the Royal School of Needlework for Her Majesty The Queen's Coronation in 1953.
Graciously loaned by Her Majesty The Queen to the Royal School of Needlework's display.
Photograph reproduced by gracious permission of Her Majesty The Queen.

The British Interior and Its Contents

A series of lectures presented for the first time by the Organisers of The Grosvenor House Antiques Fair in conjunction with The British Antique Dealers' Association.

Tuesday 16th June

10.30 a.m.	Grand Interior Decoration in the British Country House	by Geoffrey Beard Chairman, Furniture History Society. Lecturer, and author of a number of books including *Craftsmen and Interior Decoration in England* (1981) for which he was awarded the Sir Bannister Fletcher Prize.
12 noon	Burghley House and its Contents	by Lady Victoria Leatham Departmental Director of Sotheby's. Author and broadcaster. Resident curator of Burghley House.
2.30 p.m.	Antiques in a Modern Setting	by David Pettifer Antique dealer for 25 years specialising in English furniture. Lecturer aboard the QE2. President of The British Antique Dealers' Association.
4 p.m.	The Building of 'Treasure Houses'	by Gervase Jackson-Stops Worked at the Victoria & Albert Museum before joining The National Trust in 1971 as architectural adviser; is a regular contributor to *Country Life* and was curator of the 'Treasure Houses of Britain' exhibition in Washington D.C., 1985–86.

Wednesday 17th June

10.30 a.m.	The Furnishing of Ham House 1660–1760	by John Hardy Assistant Keeper in the Department of Furniture, Victoria & Albert Museum, which administers Ham House. Curator in charge of Osterley Park House. International lecturer and contributor to art magazines on furniture and interior decoration.
12 noon	The Geffrye Museum — The English Interior Displayed	by David Rodgers Curator, The Geffrye Museum. Previously worked at art galleries and museums in York, Sheffield, London, Wolverhampton and Exeter. Author of *Coronation Souvenirs and Commemoratives*.

2.30 p.m.	Some Aspects of English Needlework	by Lanto Synge Director of Mallett's. Author of *Chairs, Antique Needlework* and *The Royal School of Needlework Book of Needlework and Embroidery*. Contributor of articles to various periodicals.
4 p.m.	The Ornamental Use of Ceramics in the 18th-Century English Country House	by Anna Somers Cocks Assistant Keeper at the Victoria & Albert Museum from 1973–1986, initially with responsibility for Continental silver and jewellery and subsequently for Continental porcelain. Editor of *Apollo* magazine since early 1987.

Thursday 18th June

10.30 a.m.	Two Hundred Years of Domestic Picture Hanging in Scotland	by Timothy Clifford Director of the National Galleries of Scotland. Author of several books including *Ceramics of Derbyshire, 1750–1975* and *Turner at Manchester* (1982). Contributor to arts magazines.
12 noon	Cross-Channel Pollination in Furniture Design	by Jonathan Harris London antique dealer with a broad interest in works of art of all kinds. Vice President of The British Antique Dealers' Association.
2.30 p.m.	Interiors in Victorian Paintings	by Christopher Wood Former Director of Christie's and Head of the 19th-Century Paintings Department. Now Director of the Christopher Wood Gallery in Belgravia, specialising in Victorian and Edwardian art. Author of *The Dictionary of Victorian Paintings* among other books on Victorian art.
4 p.m.	English Silver and its American Equivalents	by David Brand Inglis Silver dealer in London for 25 years. Past President of The British Antique Dealers' Association.

The hour-long lectures will be held in the Court Suite at Grosvenor House. Tickets are £11 each and are available from the Organisers' Office at the Fair (adjacent to the foyer entrance) and from their offices on 0799 26699.

Plans Showing Exhibitors' Stands

Entrance Foyer and Great Room Balcony

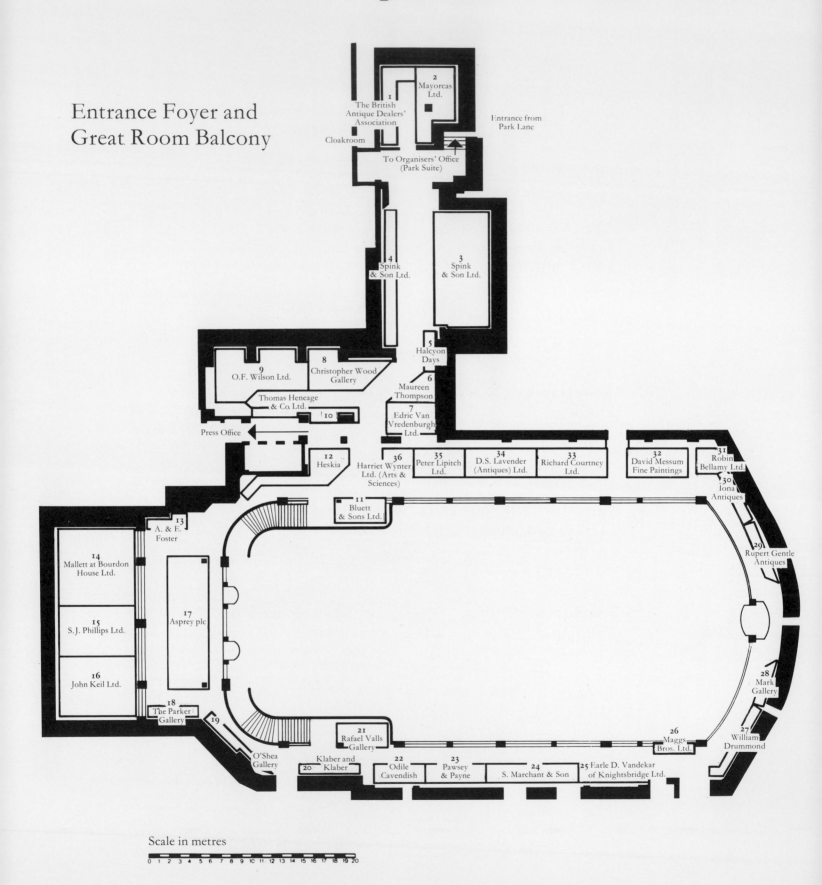

The British Antique Dealers' Association

Cloakroom

1

2 Mayorcas Ltd.

Entrance from Park Lane

To Organisers' Office (Park Suite)

4 Spink & Son Ltd.

3 Spink & Son Ltd.

5 Halcyon Days

6 Maureen Thompson

9 O.F. Wilson Ltd.

8 Christopher Wood Gallery

7 Edric Van Vredenburgh Ltd.

Thomas Heneage & Co. Ltd.

10

Press Office

12 Heskia

36 Harriet Wynter Ltd. (Arts & Sciences)

35 Peter Lipitch Ltd.

34 D.S. Lavender (Antiques) Ltd.

33 Richard Courtney Ltd.

32 David Messum Fine Paintings

31 Robin Bellamy Ltd.

30 Iona Antiques

11 Bluett & Sons Ltd.

13 A. & E. Foster

14 Mallett at Bourdon House Ltd.

29 Rupert Gentle Antiques

17 Asprey plc

15 S.J. Phillips Ltd.

16 John Keil Ltd.

28 Mark Gallery

18 The Parker Gallery

19

O'Shea Gallery

21 Rafael Valls Gallery

26 Maggs Bros. Ltd.

27 William Drummond

Klaber and Klaber

20

22 Odile Cavendish

23 Pawsey & Payne

24 S. Marchant & Son

25 Earle D. Vandekar of Knightsbridge Ltd.

Scale in metres

0 1 2 3 4 5 6 7 8 9 10 11 12 13 14 15 16 17 18 19 20

Visitors to The Grosvenor House
Antiques Fair are respectfully
reminded that, in the interests
of security, not a single exhibit
can be allowed out of the Fair
unless it is accompanied by an
official Pass-Out Form.

Great Room

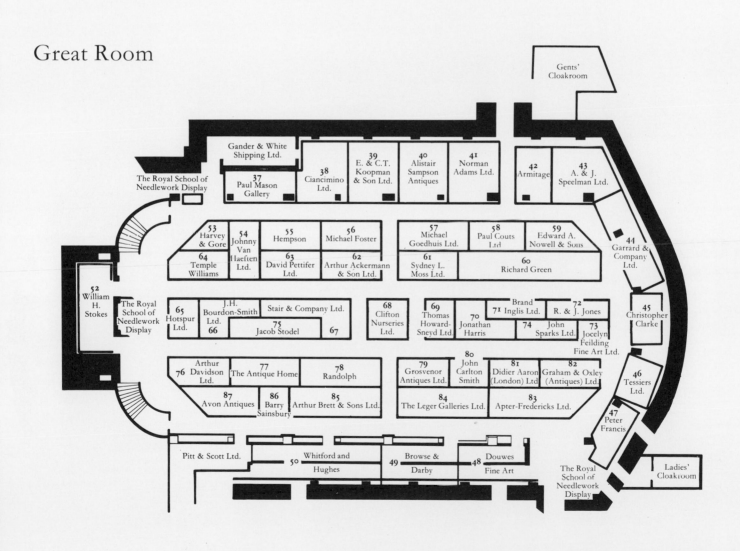

Scale in metres

0 1 2 3 4 5 6 7 8 9 10 11 12 13 14 15 16 17 18 19 20

Alphabetical List of Exhibitors

Aaron (London) Limited, Didier
21 Ryder Street, London SW1 6PX
Tel. 01-839 4716/7
Telex 28905 REF. 438
18th-century French furniture; Old Master
drawings; paintings and Oriental works of art.
STAND NO. 81
STAND TEL. 01-499 6363 *Ext.* 7187
pages 26 and 27

Ackermann & Son Limited, Arthur
3 Old Bond Street, London W1X 3TD
Tel. 01-493 3288/7647
Member: British Antique Dealers' Association
Member: Society of London Art Dealers
Paintings; drawings; prints and engravings
STAND NO. 62
STAND TEL. 01-499 6363 *Ext.* 7154
page 28

Adams Limited, Norman
8–10 Hans Road, Knightsbridge, London SW3 1RX
(Opposite west side Harrods)
Tel. 01-589 5266
Member: British Antique Dealers' Association
Furniture; clocks and barometers; glass pictures
and chandeliers
STAND NO. 41
STAND TEL. 01-499 6363 *Ext.* 7104
pages 30 and 31

Antique Home, The
104A Kensington Church Street, London W8 4BU
Tel. 01-229 5892
Member: British Antique Dealers' Association
Furniture
STAND NO. 77
STAND TEL. 01-499 6363 *Ext.* 7178
page 29

Apter-Fredericks Limited
265–267 Fulham Road, London SW3 6HY
Tel. 01-352 2188
Member: British Antique Dealers' Association
Furniture
STAND NO. 83
STAND TEL. 01-499 6363 *Ext.* 7179
page 32

Armitage
4 Davies Street, Berkeley Square, London W1Y 1LJ
Tel. 01-408 0675/01-629 0958
Member: British Antique Dealers' Association
Silver
STAND NO. 42
STAND TEL. 01-499 6363 *Ext.* 7143
pages 34 and 35

Asprey plc
165–169 New Bond Street, London W1Y 0AR
Tel. 01-493 6767
Member: British Antique Dealers' Association
Clocks and barometers; furniture; glass; jewellery,
bijouterie and snuff boxes; silver and old
Sheffield plate; Russian works of art
STAND NO. 17
STAND TEL. 01-499 6363 *Ext.* 7116
pages 36 and 37

Avon Antiques
26 & 27 Market Street, Bradford-on-Avon,
Wiltshire BA15 1LL
Tel. 02216 2052
Member: British Antique Dealers' Association
Furniture; clocks and barometers; metalwork;
textiles
STAND NO. 87
STAND TEL. 01-499 6363 *Ext.* 7016
page 38

Bellamy Limited, Robin
97 Corn Street, Witney, Oxfordshire OX8 7DL
Tel. 0993 4793
Member: British Antique Dealers' Association
Specialists in pewter and base metal; bygones,
curiosities and works of art
By appointment only
STAND NO. 31
STAND TEL. 01-499 6363 *Ext.* 7133
page 39

Bluett & Sons Limited
48 Davies Street, London W1Y 1LD
Tel. 01-629 4018/3397
Telex 8952022 CTYTEL G. ATTENTION BLUETT
Member: British Antique Dealers' Association
Oriental ceramics and works of art
STAND NO. 11
STAND TEL. 01-499 6363 *Ext.* 7153
page 40

Bourdon-Smith Limited, J.H.
24 Mason's Yard, Duke Street, St. James's,
London SW1Y 6BU
Tel. 01-839 4714/5
Member: British Antique Dealers' Association
Antique silver; snuff boxes and early spoons
STAND NO. 66
STAND TEL. 01-499 6363 *Ext.* 7160
page 41

Brett and Sons Limited, Arthur
42 St. Giles Street, Norwich, Norfolk NR2 1LW
Tel. 0603 628171
Member: British Antique Dealers' Association
Furniture; metalwork and pewter
STAND NO. 85
STAND TEL. 01-499 6363 *Ext.* 7135
page 42

British Antique Dealers' Association, The
20 Rutland Gate, London SW7 1BD
Tel. 01-589 4128
Established in 1918 to promote, protect and
further the interests of the antiques trade. The
B.A.D.A. currently represents approximately
500 of the most knowledgeable antique dealers
in the United Kingdom.
STAND NO. 1
Incorporating:
Maurice Asprey Limited
Bobinet
D.M. & P. Manheim (Peter Manheim) Limited
Steppes Hill Farm Antiques
Anthony Woodburn Limited
STAND TEL. 01-499 6363 *Ext.* 4816
pages 125–132

Browse & Darby
19 Cork Street, London W1X 2LP
Tel. 01-734 7984/5
Member: Society of London Art Dealers
Specialists in French and British paintings,
drawings and sculpture of the 19th and 20th
centuries.
STAND NO. 49
STAND TEL. 01-499 6363 *Ext.* 7039
page 44

Carlton Smith, John
17 Ryder Street, St. James's, London SW1Y 6PY
Tel. 01-930 6622
Member: British Antique Dealers' Association
Clocks and barometers
STAND NO. 80
STAND TEL. 01-499 6363 *Ext.* 7192
page 45

Cavendish, Odile
14 Lowndes Street, London SW1X 9EX
Tel. 01-243 1668
Oriental works of art; Chinese and Japanese
furniture; lacquer; sculpture; screens; paintings
By appointment only
STAND NO. 22
STAND TEL. 01-499 6363 *Ext.* 7121
page 46

Ciancimino Limited
99 Pimlico Road, London SW1W 8PH
Tel. 01-730 9950
Member: British Antique Dealers' Association
18th- and 19th-century English and Continental
furniture and works of art; fine Chinese,
Chinese export and Japanese lacquer and
screens
STAND NO. 38
STAND TEL. 01-499 6363 *Ext.* 7164
page 47

Clarke, Christopher
The Fosse Way, Stow-on-the-Wold,
    Gloucestershire GL54 1JS
Tel. 0451 30476
Member: British Antique Dealers' Association
Furniture; works of art; metalwork; needlework
STAND NO. 45
STAND TEL. 01-499 6363 *Ext.* 7170
page 49

Clifton Nurseries Limited
5a Clifton Villas, London W9 2PH
Tel. 01-289 6851
Architectural and garden items
STAND NO. 68
STAND TEL. 01-499 6363 *Ext.* 7198
page 48

Courtney Limited, Richard
112–114 Fulham Road, London SW3 6HU
Tel. 01-370 4020
Member: British Antique Dealers' Association
18th-century English furniture
STAND NO. 33
STAND TEL. 01-499 6363 *Ext.* 7002
page 50

Couts Limited, Paul
101–107 West Bow (Victoria Street),
    Edinburgh EH1 2JP, Scotland
Tel. 031-225 3238
and 80 Fulham Road, London SW3 6HR
Tel. 01-581 8226
Member: British Antique Dealers' Association
Period English furniture
STAND NO. 58
STAND TEL. 01-499 6363 *Ext.* 7169
page 51

Davidson Limited, Arthur
78/79 Jermyn Street, London SW1Y 6NB
Tel. 01-930 6687/4643
Member: British Antique Dealers' Association
Antiquities and works of art; architectural items;
    bygones, curiosities and unusual items;
    furniture; medical instruments and scientific
    instruments
STAND NO. 76
STAND TEL. 01-499 6363 *Ext.* 7177
page 52

Douwes Fine Art
38 Duke Street, St. James's, London SW1Y 6DF
Tel. 01-839 5795
Paintings and Old Master drawings
STAND NO. 48
STAND TEL. 01-499 6363 *Ext.* 7100
page 53

Drummond, William
8 St. James's Chambers, Ryder Street, London
    SW1Y 6QA
Tel. 01-930 9696
Member: British Antique Dealers' Association
Member: Society of London Art Dealers
Watercolours, drawings and oil paintings
By appointment only
STAND NO. 27
STAND TEL. 01-499 6363 *Ext.* 7119
pages 54 and 55

Feilding Fine Art Limited, Jocelyn
at the Alan Jacobs Gallery
8 Duke Street, St. James's, London SW1Y 6BN
Tel. 01-839 5040/01-930 3709
Member: Society of London Art Dealers
Paintings and watercolours
STAND NO. 73
STAND TEL. 01-499 6363 *Ext.* 7139
page 56

Foster, A. & E.
'Little Heysham', Naphill,
    Buckinghamshire HP14 4SU
Tel. 024 024 2024
Member: British Antique Dealers' Association
Treen; works of art; metalwork
By appointment only
STAND NO. 13
STAND TEL. 01-499 6363 *Ext.* 7112
page 57

Foster, Michael
118 Fulham Road, London SW3 6HU
Tel. 01-373 3636
Member: British Antique Dealers' Association
Furniture; works of art; musical instruments
STAND NO. 56
STAND TEL. 01-499 6363 *Ext.* 7145
pages 58 and 59

Francis, Peter
26 Museum Street, London WC1A 1JT
Tel. 01-637 0165
Member: British Antique Dealers' Association
Furniture and decorative items
STAND NO. 47
STAND TEL. 01-499 6363 *Ext.* 7171
page 60

**Garrard & Company Limited
(The Crown Jewellers)**
112 Regent Street, London W1A 2JJ
Tel. 01-734 7020
Member: British Antique Dealers' Association
Clocks and barometers; jewellery, bijouterie and
    snuff boxes; silver and old Sheffield plate
STAND NO. 44
STAND TEL. 01-499 6363 *Ext.* 7156
page 61

Gentle Antiques, Rupert
The Manor House, Milton Lilbourne, Pewsey,
    Wiltshire SN9 5LQ
Tel. 0672 63344
Member: British Antique Dealers' Association
Metalwork; furniture; needlework
STAND NO. 29
STAND TEL. 01-499 6363 *Ext.* 7118
page 62

**Goedhuis Limited, Michael
Colnaghi Oriental**
14 Old Bond Street, London W1X 4JL
Tel. 01-409 3324
Member: British Antique Dealers' Association
Oriental works of art
STAND NO. 57
STAND TEL. 01-499 6363 *Ext.* 7157
page 63

Graham and Oxley (Antiques) Limited
101 Kensington Church Street, London W8 7LN
Tel. 01-229 1850
Member: British Antique Dealers' Association
Porcelain, pottery, furniture and works of art
STAND NO. 82
STAND TEL. 01-499 6363 *Ext.* 7140
page 64

Green, Richard
44 Dover Street, London W1X 4JQ
and 4 New Bond Street, London W1Y 9PE
Tel. 01-493 3939
Telex 25796 Green G
New York Tel. 518-583 2060
Member: British Antique Dealers' Association
Member: Society of London Art Dealers
Old Master, sporting, marine, modern British and
    Impressionist paintings
STAND NO. 60
STAND TEL. 01-499 6363 *Ext.* 7158
pages 66 and 67

Grosvenor Antiques Limited
27 Holland Street, Kensington, London W8 4NA
Tel. 01-937 8649
Member: British Antique Dealers' Association
Porcelain, bronzes and small works of art
STAND NO. 79
STAND TEL. 01-499 6363 *Ext.* 7131
page 65

Halcyon Days
14 Brook Street, London W1Y 1AA
Tel. 01-629 8811
and 4 Royal Exchange, London EC3V 3LL
Tel. 01-626 1120
Member: British Antique Dealers' Association
Enamels; snuff boxes; objects of vertu; treen;
    porcelain and pottery; drawings and prints;
    papier mâché; tôle
STAND NO. 5
STAND TEL. 01-499 6363 *Ext.* 7195
page 68

Harris, Jonathan
54 Kensington Church Street, London w8 4DB
Tel. 01-937 3133
Member: British Antique Dealers' Association
English, Oriental and European furniture and
    works of art
STAND NO. 70
STAND TEL. 01-499 6363 *Ext.* 7188
page 69

Harvey & Gore
4 Burlington Gardens, London w1x 1LH
Tel. 01-493 2714
Member: British Antique Dealers' Association
Jewellery, bijouterie and snuff boxes; silver and
    old Sheffield plate
STAND NO. 53
STAND TEL. 01-499 6363 *Ext.* 7180
page 70

Hempson
Melchbourne Park, Melchbourne, Bedfordshire
Tel. 0234 708872
Continental furniture and works of art
By appointment only
STAND NO. 55
STAND TEL. 01-499 6363 *Ext.* 7162
page 71

Heneage & Co. Limited, Thomas
42 Duke Street, St. James's, London sw1y 6DJ
Tel. 01-930 9223/01-720 1503
Telex 297761 BTI EQ G
Art reference books and manuscripts; antiquities
    and works of art; jewellery
STAND NO. 10
STAND TEL. 01-499 6363 *Ext.* 7108
page 72

Heskia
19 Mount Street, London w1y 5RA
Tel. 01-629 1483/4
Member: British Antique Dealers' Association
Carpets and rugs
STAND NO. 12
STAND TEL. 01-499 6363 *Ext.* 7105
page 73

Hotspur Limited
14 Lowndes Street, London sw1x 9EX
Tel. 01-235 1918
Member: British Antique Dealers' Association
Furniture
STAND NO. 65
STAND TEL. 01-499 6363 *Ext.* 7009
page 74

Howard-Sneyd Limited, Thomas
35 Fursecroft, George Street, London w1y 5HG
Tel. 01-723 1976
Antiquities and works of art
By appointment only
STAND NO. 69
STAND TEL. 01-499 6363 *Ext.* 7166
page 75

Inglis Limited, Brand
9 Halkin Arcade, Motcomb Street, London sw1
Tel. 01-235 6604
Member: British Antique Dealers' Association
Silver and old Sheffield plate
STAND NO. 71
STAND TEL. 01-499 6363 *Ext.* 7141
page 76

Iona Antiques
P.O. Box 285, London w8 6HZ
Tel. 01-602 1193
Member: British Antique Dealers' Association
19th-century primitive animal paintings
By appointment only
STAND NO. 30
STAND TEL. 01-499 6363 *Ext.* 7134
page 77

Jones, R. & J.
137 Kensington Church Street, London w8 7LP
Tel. 01-221 4026
Member: British Antique Dealers' Association
Oil paintings and porcelain
STAND NO. 72
STAND TEL. 01-499 6363 *Ext.* 7168
page 78

Keil Limited, John
154 Brompton Road, London sw3 1HX
Tel. 01-589 6454
and 10 Quiet Street, Bath BA1 2JU
Member: British Antique Dealers' Association
Furniture; works of art; glass pictures
STAND NO. 16
STAND TEL. 01-499 6363 *Ext.* 7114
page 79

Klaber and Klaber
2A Bedford Gardens, Kensington Church Street,
    London w8 7EH
Tel. 01-727 4573
Member: British Antique Dealers' Association
Porcelain and enamels
STAND NO. 20
STAND TEL. 01-499 6363 *Ext.* 7107
page 80

Koopman & Son Limited, E. & C.T.
53/65 Chancery Lane, London wc2
Tel. 01-242 7624/8365
Member: British Antique Dealers' Association
Fine antique English and Continental silver
STAND NO. 39
STAND TEL. 01-499 6363 *Ext.* 7147
page 81

Lavender (Antiques) Limited, D.S.
16B Grafton Street, London w1x 3LA
Tel. 01-629 1782/01-409 2305
Member: British Antique Dealers' Association
Fine jewels; miniatures; works of art
STAND NO. 34
STAND TEL. 01-499 6363 *Ext.* 7130
page 82

Leger Galleries Limited, The
13 Old Bond Street, London w1x 3DB
Tel. 01-629 3538
Member: British Antique Dealers' Association
English paintings and watercolours; old Master
    paintings
STAND NO. 84
STAND TEL. 01-499 6363 *Ext.* 7181
page 83

Lipitch Limited, Peter
120 and 124 Fulham Road, London sw3 6HU
Tel. 01-373 3328
Member: British Antique Dealers' Association
Furniture and mirrors
STAND NO. 35
STAND TEL. 01-499 6363 *Ext.* 7127
page 84

Maggs Bros. Limited
50 Berkeley Square, London w1x 6EL
Tel. 01-493 7160
Member: British Antique Dealers' Association
Rare books, autographs, manuscripts and
    miniatures
STAND NO. 26
STAND TEL. 01-499 6363 *Ext.* 7120
page 85

Mallett at Bourdon House Limited
2 Davies Street, Berkeley Square, London w1y 1LJ
Tel. 01-629 2444
Member: British Antique Dealers' Association
Antiques and works of art; furniture
STAND NO. 14
STAND TEL. 01-499 6363 *Ext.* 7111
page 86

Marchant & Son, S.
120 Kensington Church Street, London w8 4BH
Tel. 01-229 5319
Member: British Antique Dealers' Association
Oriental ceramics and works of art
STAND NO. 24
STAND TEL. 01-499 6363 *Ext.* 7123
page 87

Mark Gallery
9 Porchester Place, Marble Arch, London W2 2BS
Tel. 01-262 4906
Member: British Antique Dealers' Association
Russian icons
STAND NO. 28
STAND TEL. 01-499 6363 *Ext.* 7117
page 88

Mason Gallery, Paul
149 Sloane Street, London SW1X 9BZ
Tel. 01-730 3683/7359
Member: British Antique Dealers' Association
18th- and 19th-century paintings; glass pictures;
    drawings, prints and engravings; picture frames
STAND NO. 37
STAND TEL. 01-499 6363 *Ext.* 7144
pages 90 and 91

Mayorcas Limited
38 Jermyn Street, London SW1Y 6DN
Tel. 01-629 4195
Member: British Antique Dealers' Association
Tapestries; needlework; textiles; European
    carpets and rugs
STAND NO. 2
STAND TEL. 01-499 6363 *Ext.* 7173
page 89

Messum Fine Paintings, David
The Studio, Lords Wood, Marlow,
    Buckinghamshire SL7 2QS
Tel. 06284 6565/6
Member: British Antique Dealers' Association
Paintings and drawings
STAND NO. 32
STAND TEL. 01-499 6363 *Ext.* 7125
page 92

Moss Limited, Sydney L.
51 Brook Street, London W1Y 1AU
Tel. 01-629 4670/01-493 7374
Member: British Antique Dealers' Association
Chinese scholastic works of art; Chinese and
    Japanese paintings; Japanese netsuke, inro and
    lacquer
STAND NO. 61
STAND TEL. 01-499 6363 *Ext.* 7159
page 93

Nowell & Sons, Edward A.
21/23 Market Place, Wells, Somerset BA5 2RF
Tel. 0749 72415
Member: British Antique Dealers' Association
Antique furniture; silver; jewellery; old Sheffield
    plate; clocks and barometers and accessories.
STAND NO. 59
STAND TEL. 01-499 6363 *Ext.* 7146
page 94

O'Shea Gallery
89 Lower Sloane Street, London SW1W 8DA
Tel. 01-730 0081/2
Member: British Antique Dealers' Association
15th–19th-century maps; topographical,
    decorative, natural history, sporting and marine
    prints; rare atlases and illustrated books; picture
    frames
STAND NO. 19
STAND TEL. 01-499 6363 *Ext.* 7021
page 95

Parker Gallery, The
12A-12B Berkeley Street, Piccadilly,
    London W1X 5AD
(Opposite Mayfair Hotel)
Tel. 01-499 5906/7
Member: British Antique Dealers' Association
Member: Society of London Art Dealers
Paintings, prints and watercolours; maps; ship
    models; pottery; bygones and curiosities
STAND NO. 18
STAND TEL. 01-499 6363 *Ext.* 7115
page 96

Pawsey & Payne
4 Ryder Street, St. James's, London SW1Y 6QB
Tel. 01-930 4221
Member: British Antique Dealers' Association
Member: Society of London Art Dealers
Drawings, prints and engravings; paintings
STAND NO. 23
STAND TEL. 01-499 6363 *Ext.* 7122
page 97

Pettifer Limited, David
269 King's Road, Chelsea, London SW3 5EN
Tel. 01-352 3088
Member: British Antique Dealers' Association
Furniture
STAND NO. 63
STAND TEL. 01-499 6363 *Ext.* 7165
page 100

Phillips Limited, S.J.
139 New Bond Street, London W1A 3DL
Tel. 01-629 6261/2
Member: British Antique Dealers' Association
Jewellery, bijouterie and snuff boxes; miniatures;
    silver and old Sheffield plate
STAND NO. 15
STAND TEL. 01-499 6363 *Ext.* 7110
pages 98 and 99

Randolph
97–99 High Street, Hadleigh, Suffolk IP7 5EJ
Tel. 0473 823789
Member: British Antique Dealers' Association
Antique furniture and accessories
STAND NO. 78
STAND TEL. 01-499 6363 *Ext.* 7176
page 101

Sainsbury Oriental Art, Barry
145 Ebury Street, London SW1
Tel. 01-730 3393
Furniture; Oriental ceramics and works of art
STAND NO. 86
STAND TEL. 01-499 6363 *Ext.* 7183
page 102

**Sampson Antiques, Alistair
(Incorporating Tobias Jellinek Antiques
Limited)**
156 Brompton Road, London SW3 1HW
Tel. 01-589 5272
Member: British Antique Dealers' Association
Oak furniture; brass; needlework; primitive
    paintings; pottery; decorative and unusual
    items; treen
STAND NO. 40
STAND TEL. 01-499 6363 *Ext.* 7148
page 103

Sparks Limited, John
128 Mount Street, London W1Y 5HA
Tel. 01-499 2265/1932
Member: British Antique Dealers' Association
Oriental ceramics and works of art
STAND NO. 74
STAND TEL. 01-499 6363 *Ext.* 7185
pages 106 and 107

Speelman Limited, A. & J.
129 Mount Street, London W1
Tel. 01-499 5126
Member: British Antique Dealers' Association
Oriental ceramics and works of art
STAND NO. 43
STAND TEL. 01-499 6363 *Ext.* 7172
page 104

Spink & Son Limited
5, 6 and 7 King Street, St. James's,
    London SW1Y 6QS
Tel. 01-930 7888
Member: British Antique Dealers' Association
Member: Society of London Art Dealers
Coins, medals and decorations; English paintings
    and watercolours; silver and jewellery; antique
    paperweights; Chinese and Japanese ceramics
    and works of art; Indian and South East Asian
    sculpture; Islamic works of art; European and
    Eastern textiles
STAND NOS. 3 and 4
STAND TELS. 01-499 6363 *Ext.* 7193, 7174
pages 108 and 109

Stair & Company Limited
120 Mount Street, London W1Y 5HB
Tel. 01-499 1784/5
and 942 Madison Avenue, New York,
N.Y. 10021
Member : British Antique Dealers' Association
18th-century English furniture and works of art;
    glass chandeliers; mirrors; clocks and
    barometers; needlework and tapestry; lamps
STAND NO. 67
STAND TEL. 01-499 6363 *Ext.* 7113
pages 110 and 111

Stodel, Jacob
116 Kensington Church Street, London W8 4BH
Tel. 01-221 2652
Member : British Antique Dealers' Association
Works of art; fine furniture; ceramics
STAND NO. 75
STAND TEL. 01-499 6363 *Ext.* 7150
page 105

Stokes, William H.
Roberts House, Siddington, Cirencester,
    Gloucestershire GL7 6EX
Tel. 0285 67101
Member : British Antique Dealers' Association
Early oak furniture
STAND NO. 52
STAND TEL. 01-499 6363 *Ext.* 7138
page 112

Tessiers Limited
26 New Bond Street, London W1Y 0JY
Tel. 01-629 0458/6405
Member : British Antique Dealers' Association
Clocks and barometers; jewellery; bijouterie and
    snuff boxes; silver and old Sheffield plate; wine
    related items
STAND NO. 46
STAND TEL. 01-499 6363 *Ext.* 7142
pages 114 and 115

Thompson, Maureen
Sun House, Long Melford, Suffolk CO10 9HZ
Tel. 0787 78252
Member : British Antique Dealers' Association
Glass
STAND NO. 6
STAND TEL. 01-499 6363 *Ext.* 7132
page 113

Valls Gallery, Rafael
6 Ryder Street, St. James's, London SW1Y 6QB
Tel. 01-930 0029
Old Master paintings
STAND NO. 21
STAND TEL. 01-499 6363 *Ext.* 7194
page 116

Vandekar of Knightsbridge Limited, Earle D.
138 Brompton Road, London SW3 1HY
Tel. 01-589 8481/3398
and 15 East 57th Street, New York, N.Y. 10022
Member : British Antique Dealers' Association
Oriental ceramics and works of art; English and
    Continental porcelain, pottery and enamels
STAND NO. 25
STAND TEL. 01-499 6363 *Ext.* 7124
page 117

Van Haeften Limited, Johnny
13 Duke Street, St. James's, London SW1Y 6DB
Tel. 01-930 3062
Member : British Antique Dealers' Association
16th- and 17th-century Dutch and Flemish Old
    Master paintings
STAND NO. 54
STAND TEL. 01-499 6363 *Ext.* 7163
page 118

Van Vredenburgh Limited, Edric
37 Bury Street, St. James's, London SW1Y 6AU
Tel. 01-839 5818
Decorative works of art of all centuries, both
    European and Oriental, specialising in
    pietra dura
STAND NO. 7
STAND TEL. 01-499 6363 *Ext.* 7106
page 119

Whitford and Hughes
6 Duke Street, St. James's, London SW1
Tel. 01-930 9332/5577
Telex 28905 REF 3338
Fax 01-839 5813
Member : Society of London Art Dealers
Paintings 1880–1920, Post-Impressionist,
    Symbolist, Vienna Secession, Salon and
    Academy, Belle-Epoque
STAND NO. 50
STAND TEL. 01-499 6363 *Ext.* 7167
page 120

Williams, Temple
34 Abingdon Road, London W8 6AS
(correspondence only)
Tel. 01-937 4677 (answering service)
Furniture and works of art
View by appointment, goods in store
STAND NO. 64
STAND TEL. 01-499 6363 *Ext.* 7161
page 121

Wilson Limited, O.F.
Queen's Elm Parade, Old Church Street,
    London SW3 6EJ
Tel. 01-352 9554
Member : British Antique Dealers' Association
English and Continental decorative furniture and
    works of art, 1760–1820; period mantelpieces;
    architectural items; drawings, prints and
    engravings
STAND NO. 9
STAND TEL. 01-499 6363 *Ext.* 7182
page 122

Wood Gallery, Christopher
15 Motcomb Street, Belgravia, London SW1X 8LB
Tel. 01-235 9141/2
Member : British Antique Dealers' Association
Member : Society of London Art Dealers
Paintings; sculpture; ceramics
STAND NO. 8
STAND TEL. 01-499 6363 *Ext.* 7175
page 123

Wynter Limited (Arts & Sciences), Harriet
50 Redcliffe Road, London SW10 9NJ
Tel. 01-352 6494
Member : British Antique Dealers' Association
Bygones, curiosities and unusual items; medical
    instruments; scientific instruments; paintings
    and prints
View by appointment only
STAND NO. 36
STAND TEL. 01-499 6363 *Ext.* 7128
page 124

Exhibitors

Didier Aaron (London) Limited

21 Ryder Street, London SW1Y 6PX
TELEPHONE 01-839 4716/7
and 118 Faubourg Saint-Honoré, 75008 Paris
and 32 East 67th Street, New York, N.Y. 10021

La Halte
by Jacques-François-Joseph Swebach
(1769 Metz – Paris 1825),
circa 1810.
Signed 'Swebach'.
Oil on canvas.
41×64 cm ($16\frac{1}{8} \times 25\frac{1}{4}$ in).

Didier Aaron (London) Limited

21 Ryder Street, London SW1Y 6PX
TELEPHONE 01-839 4716/7
and 118 Faubourg Saint-Honoré, 75008 Paris
and 32 East 67th Street, New York, N.Y. 10021

A very fine marquetry and parquetry ormolu-mounted Louis XV/XVI Transition commode.
Stamped J.H. RIESENER (Maitre in 1768).
Height 90 cm (35½ in) Width 147 cm (58 in) Depth 62 cm (24½ in).

Arthur Ackermann & Son Limited

3 Old Bond Street, London W1X 3TD

TELEPHONE 01-493 3288/7647

The Farmyard by John Frederick Herring, Senior (1795–1865).
On panel, signed and dated 1840.
54.6 × 76.2 cm (21½ × 30 in).

The Antique Home

104A Kensington Church Street, London W8 4BU

TELEPHONE 01-229 5892

A fine Queen Anne period walnut bachelor's chest of pleasing proportions and good colour.
Circa 1710. Height 75 cm (29½ in) Width 76 cm (30 in) Depth 33 cm (13 in).
A rare early 18th-century miniature walnut side chair inlaid with ivory and various woods.
Circa 1740. Height 39 cm (15 in).

Norman Adams Limited

8–10 Hans Road, Knightsbridge, London SW3 1RX
TELEPHONE 01-589 5266

A beautifully restrained Chippendale period serpentine mahogany commode.
Circa 1760.
Height 82.5 cm (32 in) Width 101.5 cm (40 in) Depth 55.2 cm (21½ in).

Norman Adams Limited

8–10 Hans Road, Knightsbridge, London SW3 1RX

TELEPHONE 01-589 5266

An extremely rare Sheraton period sofa table with original lacquered decoration
in unusually good state. Circa 1790.
Height 70 cm (27½ in) Width (closed) 99 cm (39 in) Width (open) 146 cm (57½ in) Depth 55.8 cm (22 in).

Apter-Fredericks Limited

265–267 Fulham Road, London sw3 6hy

TELEPHONE 01-352 2188

A rare and important pair of George II carved mahogany armchairs.
Attributable to M. Darly. England, circa 1755.

Apter-Fredericks Limited

265–267 Fulham Road, London SW3 6HY

TELEPHONE 01-352 2188

A very rare George II padouk-wood bureau on parcel-gilt stand.
England, circa 1745. Exhibited: Art Treasures Exhibition, Bath 1958.

Armitage

4 Davies Street, Berkeley Square, London W1Y 1LJ
TELEPHONE 01-408 0675/01-629 0958

An important chinoiserie tankard by John Sutton. London, 1683.

Armitage

4 Davies Street, Berkeley Square, London W1Y 1LJ
TELEPHONE 01-408 0675/01-629 0958

A fine George II teakettle on stand by Paul de Lamerie. London, 1742–46.

Asprey plc

165–169 New Bond Street, London W1Y 0AR

TELEPHONE 01-493 6767

A fine George III bombe marquetry commode in the manner of John Cobb,
with good gilt brass mounts.
English, circa 1775.
Width 104 cm (3 ft 5 in).
A fine silver-mounted ebonised bracket clock by Daniel Quare.
English, circa 1710. Height 43 cm (1 ft 5 in).
A pair of George I candlesticks by Joseph Barbutt.
1719. Weight 24 oz.

Asprey plc
165–169 New Bond Street, London W1Y 0AR
TELEPHONE 01-493 6767

A rare Charles II tobacco box by Wolfgang Howzer embossed with the arms of Robert Hanson, Lord Mayor of London in 1672.

A fine Victorian gold chalice, set with sapphires by John Hardman and Co., Birmingham, circa 1865. Height 18.4 cm (7¼ in) Weight 12¼ oz.

'Wellspring' glass carafe, designed by R. Redgrave A.R.A. and made by I.F. Christy for Summerly's Art Manufactures. Signed, circa 1847.

Ribbed glass wine funnel. Second half 18th century.

A rare William IV cast limpet shell caddy spoon by William Traies. 1831.

A George III silver-gilt foxhead stirrup cup by Peter and Anne Bateman. 1798.

Russian silver and niello snuff-box with gold plaque depicting Mikhaylovsky Palace. Moscow, 1843. Width 8.3 cm (3¼ in).

Extremely rare glass-lipped ladle with moulded bowl. Mid 18th century.

Avon Antiques

26 & 27 Market Street, Bradford-on-Avon, Wiltshire BA15 1LL

TELEPHONE 02216 2052

George III mahogany tea table, circa 1780.
Height 69 cm (27 in) Width 90 cm (35 in) Depth 59 cm (23 in).

Robin Bellamy Limited

97 Corn Street, Witney, Oxfordshire OX8 7DL
TELEPHONE 0993 4793

Pair of Northern European latten candlesticks.
Circa 1500.

Bluett & Sons Limited

48 Davies Street, London W1Y 1LD
TELEPHONE 01-629 4018/3397

Annamese large stoneware dish decorated in underglaze blue and overglaze enamels and gilt.
16th century. Diameter 35.8 cm (14 in).

J. H. Bourdon-Smith Limited

24 Mason's Yard, Duke Street, St. James's, London SW1Y 6BU

TELEPHONE 01-839 4714/5

The Rajah of Coorg's rare silver coffee cans and saucers. Made in London in 1801 by Robert, David and Samuel Hennell. Shown with other collector's pieces.

Arthur Brett and Sons Limited

42 St. Giles Street, Norwich, Norfolk NR2 1LW

TELEPHONE 0603 628171

Superb semi-elliptical commode in harewood, satinwood, burr yew tree and other woods,
with high quality ormolu mounts, in the style of Robert Adam. Circa 1785.
Height 88.9 cm (35 in) Width 162.6 cm (64 in) Depth 63.5 cm (25 in).
For similar commodes see 'Three Remarkable Cabinets' by Edward H. Pinto in *The Antique Collector*, October 1957
and 'The Derby House Commode' by Hugh Roberts in *The Burlington Magazine*, May 1985.

The British Antique Dealers' Association

20 Rutland Gate, London SW7 1BD

TELEPHONE 01-589 4128

The exhibits on Stand 1 are offered for sale
by various members of the British Antique Dealers' Association
(see pages 125–132).
A full list of members is available on request
from the Association at the above address.

Browse & Darby

19 Cork Street, London WIX 2LP
TELEPHONE 01-734 7984/5

St. Jacques, Dieppe, South Façade by Walter Richard Sickert, circa 1900.
Oil on canvas. 55.2 × 45.7 cm (21¾ × 18 in).
Provenance: Stuart G. Bennett, Ontario.
Literature: *Sickert* by Wendy Baron, 1973, page 321, no. 116, pl. 82.

John Carlton Smith

17 Ryder Street, St. James's, London sw1y 6py

TELEPHONE 01-930 6622

A fine and small 17th-century quarter striking gilt-mounted ebony bracket clock by Joseph Knibb.
London, circa 1685. The latched movement with vase shaped pillars, skeletonised chapter ring with
numbered minutes and striking the quarters on a single bell. Height 30.5 cm (12 in).

Odile Cavendish

14 Lowndes Street, London SW1X 9EX

TELEPHONE 01-243 1668

A *Sagejubako* or Japanese picnic box containing a tiered food box, a sake
bottle and a small tray. A fine example of elaborate lacquer ware.
Edo period, 18th century. Height 30 cm (12 in).

Ciancimino Limited

99 Pimlico Road, London SW1W 8PH

TELEPHONE 01-730 9950

Fleur-de-pêche marble centre table on three finely carved lion monopodia.
Probably Italian, circa 1810.
Height 104 cm (41 in) Diameter of top 101 cm (39¾ in).

Clifton Nurseries Limited

5A Clifton Villas, London W9 2PH

TELEPHONE 01-289 6851

Display garden at our Nursery in Little Venice.

Christopher Clarke Antiques

The Fosse Way, Stow-on-the-Wold, Gloucestershire GL54 1JS

TELEPHONE 0451 30476

A fine Regency gilt library chair and
a pair of 19th-century Chinese lacquer garden seats.

Richard Courtney Limited

112–114 Fulham Road, London SW3 6HU

TELEPHONE 01-370 4020

An outstanding George I period burr walnut bureau bookcase.
English, circa 1725. Height 167.6 cm (7 ft 2 in) Width 99 cm (3 ft 3 in).

Paul Couts Limited

101–107 West Bow (Victoria Street), Edinburgh EH1 2JP, Scotland
TELEPHONE 031-225 3238
and 80 Fulham Road, London SW3 6HR
TELEPHONE 01-581 8226

An oval satinwood Pembroke table.
Circa 1790.

Arthur Davidson Limited

78–79 Jermyn Street, London SW1Y 6NB
TELEPHONE 01-930 6687/4643

A fine late 17th-century walnut relief of Hercules and Louis XIV.

Douwes Fine Art Limited

38 Duke Street, St. James's, London SW1Y 6DF
TELEPHONE 01-839 5795

Panorama near Haarlem by Jacob van Mosscher (active 1635–1655).
Dutch school. Fully signed.
Oil on panel, 52 × 84 cm (20½ × 33 in).

William Drummond

8 St. James's Chambers, Ryder Street, London SW1Y 6QA (by appointment only)
TELEPHONE 01-930 9696

Will your Honour buy a sweet Nosegay or a Memorandum Book by Paul Sandby R.A. (1731–1809).
Design for the "Twelve Cries of London", 1760, not published.
Watercolours and pencil. 17.5 × 12.5 cm (6⅞ × 4⅞ in).
See *Paul Sandby*, Yale Center, 1985, pp. 46, 47. From the collection of Lord Bruce.

William Drummond

8 St. James's Chambers, Ryder Street, London SW1Y 6QA (by appointment only)
TELEPHONE 01-930 9696

Carlton House Palace, The Circular Room by Charles Wild O.W.S. (1781–1835).
Watercolours and bodycolour. 46 × 38 cm (18 × 14¾ in).
See *The History of the Royal Residences* by W. H. Pyne, 1819, Vol III.
pp. 11, 12. An alternative design for the plate.

Jocelyn Feilding Fine Art Limited

at the Alan Jacobs Gallery, 8 Duke Street, St. James's, London SW1Y 6BN

TELEPHONE 01-839 5040/01-589 0331

Purple Galinule by Peter Paillou (fl. 1740–90).
Oil on paper. 22 × 14 cm (8¾ × 5½ in).

A. & E. Foster

"Little Heysham", Naphill, Buckinghamshire HP14 4SU
TELEPHONE 024 024 2024

Part of a collection of rare treen tobacco boxes.
English, 17th and 18th century.

Michael Foster

118 Fulham Road, London SW3 6HU

TELEPHONE 01-373 3636

A very important and rare set of eight decorated Sheraton armchairs,
each chair featuring a different panel painted with English garden
flowers within a pipped border. Circa 1780.

Michael Foster

118 Fulham Road, London SW3 6HU

TELEPHONE 01-373 3636

Height 80 cm (31½ in)
Width 53 cm (21 in)
Depth 49 cm (19 in).

Peter Francis

26 Museum Street, London WC1A 1JT

TELEPHONE 01-637 0165

A rare and interesting carved and inlaid walnut hanging watch case. Incorporating mechanism to activate strike repeat.
The carcase made of oak. Probably Holland. Circa 1720.
Height 29.5 cm (11½ in) Width 13.7 cm (5½ in) Depth 6.0 cm (2¼ in).

Garrard & Company Limited
(The Crown Jewellers)
112 Regent Street, London WIA 2JJ
TELEPHONE 01-734 7020

William IV silver centrepiece engraved with the arms of Macloughlin, Ballythomas.
By Robert Garrard, 1831 (basket 1835).
Height 58.4 cm (23 in).

Rupert Gentle Antiques

The Manor House, Milton Lilbourne, Pewsey, Wiltshire SN9 5LQ
TELEPHONE 0672 63344

An 18th-century curled paper picture of flowers. Circa 1780.
Height 45.7 cm (18 in) Width 36.2 cm (14¼ in) Depth 5.7 cm (2¼ in).

Michael Goedhuis Limited

Colnaghi Oriental

14 Old Bond Street, London W1X 4JL

TELEPHONE 01-409 3324

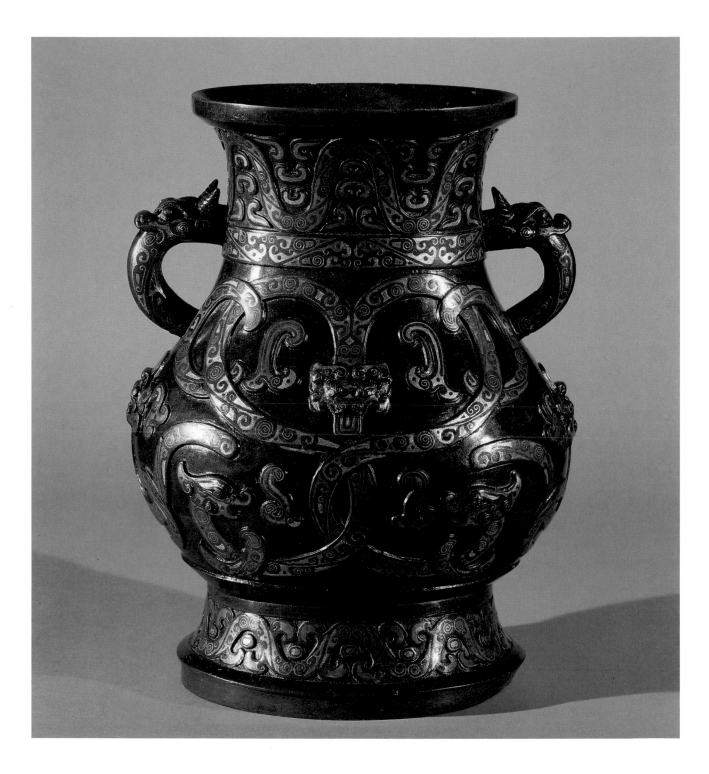

Bronze vase of Hu form inlaid in gold and silver. China, Ming dynasty
(1368–1644) or earlier. Height 31 cm (12¼ in) Width 24 cm (9½ in).

Graham & Oxley (Antiques) Limited

101 Kensington Church Street, London W8 7LN

TELEPHONE 01-229 1850

Important pair of Caughley porcelain fruit coolers, covers and liners decorated at the Chamberlains Worcester factory with the 'Bengal Tiger' pattern, bearing the arms of Coulthard of Scotby impaled Barlow. Circa 1790.

Grosvenor Antiques Limited

27 Holland Street, Kensington, London W8 4NA
TELEPHONE 01-937 8649

An important pair of French bronze and ormolu urns on Siena marble bases.
Circa 1820. Height 46 cm (18 in).

Richard Green

44 Dover Street, London WIX 4JQ
and 4 New Bond Street, London WIY 9PE
TELEPHONE 01-493 3939
NEW YORK TELEPHONE 518-583 2060

Huntsmen halting at an inn by Philips Wouwerman (1619 – Haarlem–1668).
Signed with monogram. Oil on canvas. 66 × 81.2 cm (26 × 32 in).
Provenance: Count Schönborn, Schloss Weissenstein, Pommersfelden; Sale, Paris, 17th May, 1867, lot 135
Earl of Dudley, his sale, Christie's, 25th June, 1892, lot 26, illustrated.
Exhibited: Royal Academy, Winter Exhibition, London, 1871, no. 343;
Royal Academy, Winter Exhibition, London, 1894, no. 63.
Literature: C. Hofstede de Groot, *A Catalogue Raisonné of the Works of the Most Eminent Dutch Painters
of the Seventeenth Century*, Vol. II. 1909, pp. 463–464, no. 667 and p. 625, no. 1118e.

Richard Green

44 Dover Street, London w1x 4jq
and 4 New Bond Street, London w1y 9pe
TELEPHONE 01-493 3939
NEW YORK TELEPHONE 518-583 2060

Roses by Henri Fantin-Latour (Grenoble 1836–1904 Buré).
Signed and dated '85. Oil on canvas. 31.7 × 46.5 cm (12½ × 18⅜ in).
Provenance: Mrs. Edwin Edwards, London;
Christie's, London, July 4, 1913, no. 94; Wallis & Son, London.
Literature: Mme. V. Fantin-Latour, *Catalogue de l'oeuvre complet de Fantin-Latour*,
Paris, 1911, p. 125, no. 1216. To be included in the forthcoming Fantin-Latour
catalogue raisonné being prepared by Philippe Brame and Bernard Lorenceau.

Halcyon Days

14 Brook Street, London W1Y 1AA
and 4 Royal Exchange, London EC3V 3LL
TELEPHONE 01-629 8811

An exceptional group of sculptural Bilston enamel *bonbonnières* of bird and animal form,
includes a pair of finches, a swan (the rarest of the genre), and a diminutive leopard's head.
Each one is naturalistically painted and has an associated scene on the lid.
Circa 1770.

Jonathan Harris

54 Kensington Church Street, London W8 4DB
TELEPHONE 01-937 3133

Side or dressing table in exotic hardwoods attributed
to Thomas Chippendale. Circa 1770.
Height 83.8 cm (33 in) Width 147.3 cm (58 in) Depth 67.3 cm (26½ in).

Harvey & Gore

4 Burlington Gardens, London WIX ILH

TELEPHONE OI-493 2714

A rare 18th-century rose diamond suite of brooch and pair of earrings.
French, circa 1710–20.
With original case.

Hempson

Melchbourne Park, Melchbourne, Bedfordshire

TELEPHONE 0234 708872

An important Russian Imperial malachite vase, mounted in gilt bronze. Circa 1820. Height 92.7 cm (36½ in).
Provenance: Tsar Nicholas I at Tsarskoye-Selo; presented by Nicholas to his third daughter Grand Duchess Olga
on her marriage to King Karl I of Wurttemburg; King Wilhelm II of Wurttemburg (see collection label);
the French Ambassador to St. Petersburg and Madame Jean Herbette.

Thomas Heneage & Co. Limited

42 Duke Street, St. James's, London SW1Y 6DJ

TELEPHONE 01-930 9223/01-720 1503

Rare, out-of-print and new books on the fine,
applied, and decorative arts.

Heskia

19 Mount Street, London w 1 y 5 ra
TELEPHONE 01-629 1483/4

A fine Caucasian mid nineteenth-century Shirvan rug.
A rare example of harmonious design and colour inspiration.
137 × 118 cm (4 ft 6 in × 3 ft 10 in).
(See Plate 72 Schurmann.)

Hotspur Limited

14 Lowndes Street, London SWIX 9EX

TELEPHONE 01-235 1918

An important 18th-century Adam period cut-glass chandelier of the finest quality.
Circa 1770.
Height 173 cm (5 ft 8 in) Width 112 cm (3 ft 8 in).

Thomas Howard-Sneyd Limited

35 Fursecroft, George Street, London W1Y 5HG
TELEPHONE 01-723 1976

Attic Black Figure neck-amphora by the Acheloos Painter.
Herakles steps on to a podium, kithara in hand; Athena stands on right, Dionysus and a seated attendant on left.
Circa 510 BC. Height 43.8 cm (17¼ in).

Brand Inglis Limited

9 Halkin Arcade, Motcomb Street, London SW1

TELEPHONE 01-235 6604

A Charles II cup and cover in silver by Wolfgang Howzer.
London, 1673.
Height 22.9 cm (9 in).

Iona Antiques

P.O. Box 285, London w8 6hz

TELEPHONE 01-602 1193

Three prize sheep in a landscape by W.H. Davis.
Signed and dated 1861.
Oil on canvas, 56 × 76 cm (22 × 30 in).

R. & J. Jones
137 Kensington Church Street, London W8 7LP
TELEPHONE 01-221 4026

View in the Roman Campagna
by Hendrik Frans Van Lint
(1684–1763).
One of a pair, both signed and dated 1726.
Oil on canvas.
21.5 × 26.5 cm (8½ × 10½ in).
Provenance: General William Scott, 1815 (commanded the Scots Guards at
Waterloo and bought these paintings while a prisoner of war on license);
by family descent to Major N.H. Hambro.

John Keil Limited

154 Brompton Road, London SW3 1HX
TELEPHONE 01-589 6454
and at 10 Quiet Street, Bath BA1 2JU

A fine George III mahogany breakfront bookcase of excellent colour and patination. Circa 1790.
Height 285 cm (112 in) Width 310 cm (122 in) Depth 41 cm (16 in). Provenance: Islay House, Argyll, Scotland.

Klaber and Klaber

2A Bedford Gardens, Kensington Church Street, London W8 7EH

TELEPHONE 01-727 4573

An early Derby chinoiserie group representing "Touch" from the set of Chinese senses.
Andrew Planché, "dry edge" period. Circa 1750–55.

E. & C. T. Koopman & Son Limited

53–65 Chancery Lane, London WC2
TELEPHONE 01-242 7624/8365

An exceptionally fine George III epergne by Thomas Pitts. London 1787.
The arms are those of Wright, of Plowland in Holderness, Yorkshire,
with those of another on an escutcheon of pretence.
Height 57.2 cm (22½ in) Length 54 cm (21¼ in) Weight 213 oz 10 dwt.

D.S. Lavender (Antiques) Limited

16B Grafton Street, London W1X 3LA
TELEPHONE 01-629 1782/01-409 2305

A rare Queen Anne gold snuffbox by Michael Cabaret Lagarene, St. Martin-in-the-Fields.
Signed by the goldsmith M. LAGARENE. Circa 1710.
An interesting late 18th-century snuffbox. Inset overall with ballooning scenes. Austrian, circa 1795.

The Leger Galleries Limited

13 Old Bond Street, London W1X 3DB

TELEPHONE 01-629 3538

The *Custance Conversation Piece* by Sir William Beechey, R.A. (1753–1839).
Circa 1785. Oil on canvas.
68.6 × 54.9 cm (27 × 21⅝ in).

Peter Lipitch Limited

120 and 124 Fulham Road, London SW3 6HU

TELEPHONE 01-373 3328

A rare Chippendale mahogany writing cabinet in original condition.
Circa 1760.
Width 91 cm (36 in).

Maggs Bros. Limited

50 Berkeley Square, London W1X 6EL
TELEPHONE 01-493 7160

Captain Cook's Third Voyage (1784)
bound in contemporary full dark blue morocco, gilt.
Exceptionally rare in this condition.

Mallett at Bourdon House Limited

2 Davies Street, Berkeley Square, London W1Y 1LJ

TELEPHONE 01-629 2444

A very important 17th-century Florentine *pietra dura* ebonised cabinet, profusely inlaid with
semi-precious stones depicting birds and fruit, together with marble mosaic landscape panels
and two views of the Piazza Signoria and the Medici Villa La Petraia, the columns inlaid with lapis
lazuli and having ormolu bases and capitals. Attributed to Domenico Benotti (active 1640–1653).
Height 226 cm (89 in) Width 124 cm (49 in) Depth 66 cm (26 in).

S. Marchant & Son

120 Kensington Church Street, London W8 4BH

TELEPHONE 01-229 5319

A rare Chinese porcelain imperial dragon vase
with a carved Jiaqing seal mark.
1796–1820.
Height 31.8 cm (12½ in).

Mark Gallery

9 Porchester Place, Marble Arch, London W2 2BS

TELEPHONE 01-262 4906

St. Nicholas of Mozhaisk with scenes of his life.
Central Russian icon. Late 17th century.
31.5 × 28 cm (12½ × 11 in).

Mayorcas Limited

38 Jermyn Street, St. James's, London SW1Y 6DN

TELEPHONE 01-629 4195

Exceptionally rare Dutch (Gouda) tapestry-woven table carpet *(tapis de table)* in good condition. Circa 1675.
277 × 177 cm (9 ft 1 in × 5 ft 10 in).
Similar examples at Rijksmuseum, Amsterdam and at The Art Institute of Chicago, U.S.A.

Paul Mason Gallery

149 Sloane Street, London SW1X 9BZ
TELEPHONE 01-730 3683/7359

(Above)   (Opposite page)
Amoy   *Hong Kong*
Canton   *Macao*

Paul Mason Gallery

149 Sloane Street, London SW1X 9BZ
TELEPHONE 01-730 3683/7359

A set of four late 19th-century China Trade oil paintings on canvas
showing extensive waterfront views with Chinese and foreign shipping.
Canvas 46 × 78 cm (18 × 30¾ in).

David Messum Fine Paintings

The Studio, Lords Wood, Marlow, Buckinghamshire SL7 2QS
TELEPHONE 06284 6565/6

The Garden Figure
by Stanhope Alexander Forbes R.A., N.E.A.C. (1857–1947).
Signed and dated 1916. Oil on canvas. 61 × 50.8 cm (24 × 20 in).
Exhibited: Royal Academy 1916 No. 749.

Sydney L. Moss Limited

51 Brook Street, London WIY IAU
TELEPHONE 01-629 4670/01-493 7374

An extremely rare Chinese black stone inkstone and cover with striding winged chimera surmount.
Eastern Han dynasty, circa 2nd century AD.
Height 15.9 cm (6¼ in) Diameter 13.7 cm (5⅜ in).

Edward A. Nowell & Sons

21–23 Market Place, Wells, Somerset BA5 2RF

TELEPHONE 0749 72415

A mid 18th-century Irish tea table with the unusual feature of a full slide.
Circa 1760.
A Kang Hxi blue-and-white censor. Circa 1690.
A George II period silver kettle on stand by William Partis.
Newcastle, 1742.

O'Shea Gallery

89 Lower Sloane Street, London SW1W 8DA
TELEPHONE 01-730 0081/2

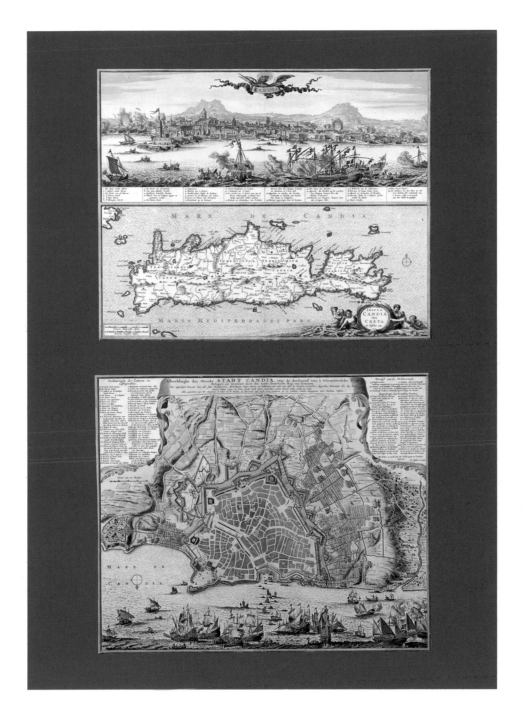

Afbeeldinghe der Stercke STADT CANDIA and *INSULA CANDIA olim CRETA* by Nicolas Visscher (1618–79).
A pair of engravings depicting the battle fleets of the Republic of Venice and the Ottoman Empire
engaged in combat before the city of Candia (Herakleion) for control of Crete in 1669.
Fine original colour heightened with gold leaf, in the style of illumination, performed by
the Dutch master-colourist Dirck Jansz van Santen (1637/8–1708). Printed in Amsterdam circa 1669.

The Parker Gallery

12A–12B Berkeley Street, Piccadilly, London WIX 5AD
TELEPHONE 01-499 5906/7

Fishing Vessels off Yarmouth, oil painting on canvas signed F. Calvert. Circa 1830.
Antique waterline model of a 32-gun Snow. Circa 1800.
Bronze statuette of an Officer of the Royal Horse Artillery. Circa 1890.
An ebony octant with ivory scale. Maker Watkins and Hill, Charing Cross. Circa 1825.
A travelling compass. Maker John Addison, London. Circa 1830.

Pawsey & Payne

4 Ryder Street, St. James's, London SW1Y 6QB

TELEPHONE 01-930 4221

The Market Cart by Dean Wolstenholme Snr.
(1757–1837) English.
Oil on canvas, signed.
35.6 × 45.7 cm (14 × 18 in).
Illustrated in *The Old English Landscape Painters*
by Colonel M.H. Grant, vol. IV, plate 164, no. 330.

S.J. Phillips Limited

139 New Bond Street, London W 1A 3DL

TELEPHONE 01-629 6261/2

George I silver-gilt bowl and cover by Benjamin Pyne. London, 1725. Height 6.5 cm (2½ in) Weight 5.85 oz.
Louis XV gold and mother-of-pearl box. Paris, 1743. Height 3.6 cm (1⅜ in) Length 7.8 cm (2⅝ in).
Antique ruby and diamond cluster necklace. Circa 1800. Length 39.5 cm (15½ in).

S.J. Phillips Limited

139 New Bond Street, London W1A 3DL

TELEPHONE 01-629 6261/2

16th-century German parcel-gilt bowl by Peter Ewerth. Anklam
(Pomerania). Circa 1580. Length 30 cm (11¾ in) Weight 16 oz.

David Pettifer Limited

269 King's Road, Chelsea, London SW3 5EN
TELEPHONE 01-352 3088

A fine Regency rosewood sofa table with ormolu mounts. Circa 1810.
Length 153 cm (60 in) Width 68 cm (27 in) Height 74 cm (29 in).

Randolph

97–99 High Street, Hadleigh, Suffolk IP7 5EJ
TELEPHONE 0473 823789

George III period small mahogany serpentine front sideboard. Circa 1785.
Height 91.4 cm (36 in) Width 121.9 cm (48 in) Depth 59.7 cm (23½ in).
George III period oval giltwood mirror. Circa 1765. Height 124.5 cm (49 in) Width 71.1 cm (28 in).

Barry Sainsbury Oriental Art

145 Ebury Street, London SW1

TELEPHONE 01-730 3393

A *hung-mu* brushpot in the form of two interlocking scrolls with a painted ribbon tie.
Chinese, Yung-cheng (1723–36).

Alistair Sampson Antiques
(Incorporating Tobias Jellinek Antiques)
156 Brompton Road, London SW3 1HW
TELEPHONE 01-589 5272

English rolled paper work. Arms of Charles II. Circa 1660.
35.6 × 28.6 cm (14 × 11¼ in) overall.

A. & J. Speelman Limited

129 Mount Street, London W1

TELEPHONE 01-499 5126

A very rare pair of *famille verte* Buddhistic lions.
K'ang Hsi period, late 17th century. Height 55.9 cm (22½ in).

Jacob Stodel

116 Kensington Church Street, London W8 4BH

TELEPHONE 01-221 2652

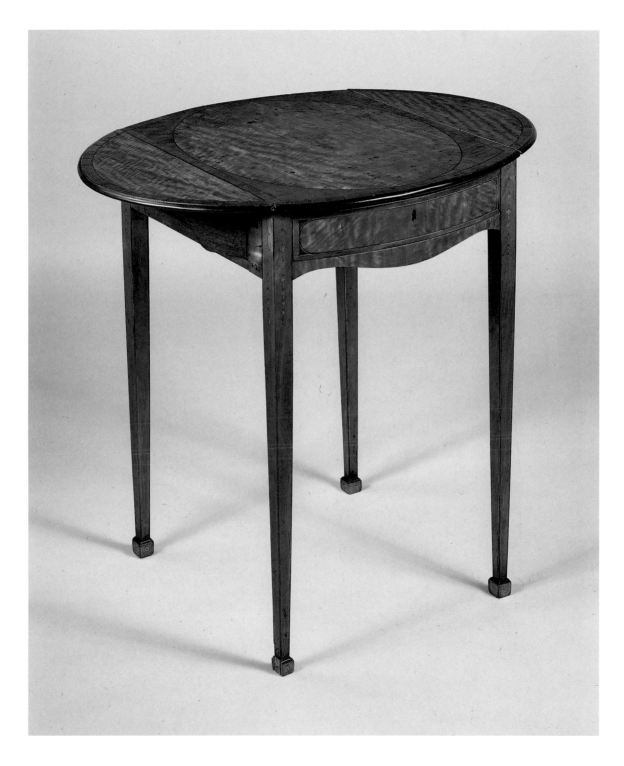

Small Sheraton oval harewood and satinwood Pembroke table.
Circa 1785. Width 70.6 cm (30 in) fully extended.

John Sparks Limited

128 Mount Street, London W 1Y 5HA
TELEPHONE 01-499 2265/1932

A Chinese carved soapstone figure of Shou Lao, God of Long Life,
standing on a contemporary rock-work base. Circa 1700. Height 39.4 cm (15 ½ in).

John Sparks Limited

128 Mount Street, London WIY 5HA

TELEPHONE 01-499 2265/1932

A Chinese painting on doeskin,
depicting a festival scene of two figures
masquerading as a Lion
and accompanied by a band of musicians,
watched by figures in a pavilion;
the scene within a shaped reserve against a ground
of lotus with exotic birds in the spandrels.
17th century.
117 × 173 cm (46 × 68 in).

Spink & Son Limited

5, 6 and 7 King Street, St. James's, London sw1y 6qs

TELEPHONE 01-930 7888

(Above) A pair of extremely rare porcelain figures of boys wearing short tunics over baggy trousers,
each with a small dog at his feet and holding up their hands, with a vase in one hand.
Each figure is supported on an ormolu base. Japanese, Arita, late 17th century.
Height 35.4 cm (14 in).

(Opposite) A pair of silver soup tureens and ladles by Paul De Lamerie. London, 1743.
From the celebrated dinner service commissioned by the 7th Earl of Thanet.
Total weight: 266 oz 4 dwt.

Stair & Company Limited

120 Mount Street, London W1Y 5HB
TELEPHONE 01-499 1784/5
and 942 Madison Avenue, New York, N.Y. 10021

Stair & Company Limited

120 Mount Street, London WIY 5HB

TELEPHONE 01-499 1784/5

and 942 Madison Avenue, New York, N.Y. 10021

(Above) A magnificent rosewood veneered library table with two drawers in the
frieze and having excellent brass inlay and ormolu mounts, those at the
corners directly taken from *Household Furniture and Interior Decoration*
by Thomas Hope, 1807, Plate 41 (2). English, circa 1815.
Height 76 cm (30 in) Width 109 cm (43 in) Depth 66 cm (26 in).

(Opposite) A superb draughtsman's pedestal table veneered with well-figured
mahogany. Drawers inset with alphabetically lettered plaques.
The top drawer with a writing slide above a fitted interior and stamped
'Gillows Lancaster'. English, circa 1795. Height 95 cm (37½ in)
Width 127 cm (50 in) Depth 71 cm (28 in).

William H. Stokes

Roberts House, Siddington, Cirencester, Gloucestershire GL7 6EX

TELEPHONE 0285 67101

A fine Charles I carved oak armchair, of excellent colour and patination.
Circa 1630. Together with other pieces and objects of the period.

Maureen Thompson

Sun House, Long Melford, Suffolk, CO10 9HZ

TELEPHONE 0787 78252

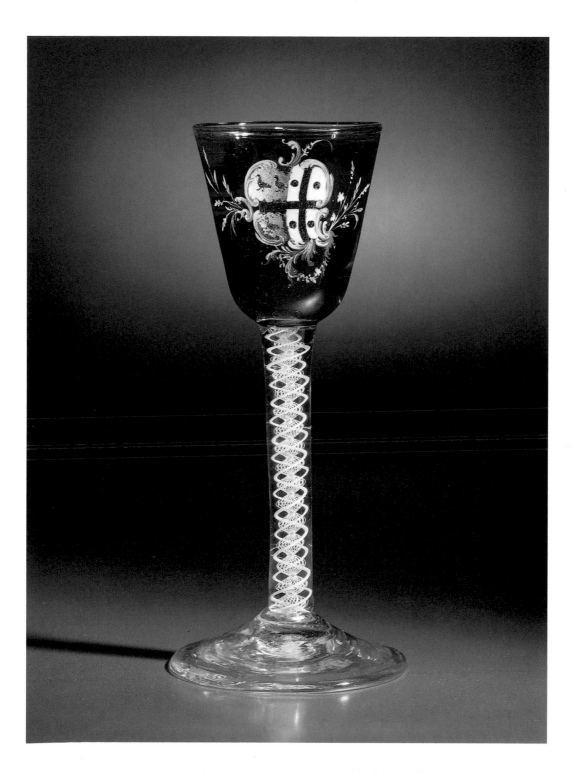

A rare enamelled armorial wine glass by Beilby of Newcastle.
English, circa 1770. Height 15 cm (6 in).

Tessiers Limited

26 New Bond Street, London W1Y 0JY

TELEPHONE 01-629 0458/6405

(Above) A fine antique emerald and diamond cluster brooch/pendant
on a graduated diamond Rivière.
Circa 1860.

(Opposite page)
A fine George II pierced silver oval swing-handle basket.
By Edward Wakelin. London, 1756.
Crest of Frankland.
Length 38.4 cm (15⅛ in).

Rafael Valls Gallery

6 Ryder Street, St. James's, London SW1Y 6QB

TELEPHONE 01-930 0029

An Extensive Landscape with the Death of the Disobedient Prophet,
by Jacob Savery (circa 1545–1602), Dutch School.
Gouache heightened with gold on
vellum laid down on panel.
Signed and dated in gold
'ISAWRIJ' (IS in monogram) '1587'.
14.2 × 25.6 cm (5½ × 10 in).

Earle D. Vandekar of Knightsbridge Limited

138 Brompton Road, London SW3 1HY
TELEPHONE 01-589 8481/3398
and 15 East 57th Street (second floor), New York, N.Y. 10022
TELEPHONE 212-308 2022

A fine pair of Qianlong *famille rose* baluster vases and covers decorated with phoenix birds.
Circa 1745. Height 55.9 cm (22 in).

Dutch interior by Pieter de Hooch (Rotterdam 1629–1681 Haarlem).
A nursemaid holding a baby in an interior,
a young girl preparing a cradle on the left.
Signed. Oil on canvas. 51.4 × 53.5 cm (20¼ × 21 in).

Edric Van Vredenburgh Limited

37 Bury Street, London SW1Y 6AU
TELEPHONE 01-839 5818

An interesting small early 19th-century mahogany collector's cabinet.
The exterior finely painted with shells and butterflies,
the interior containing a collection of shells in eight drawers.
Height 56 cm (22 in) Width 64 cm (25¼ in) Depth 31 cm (12¼ in).

Whitford and Hughes

6 Duke Street, St. James's, London SW1

TELEPHONE 01-930 9332/5577

Petit Pierre by Georges Lemmen (1865–1916). Belgian.
Oil on canvas. 95 × 95 cm (37½ × 37½ in).

Temple Williams

34 Abingdon Road, Kensington, London w8 6as (correspondence only)

TELEPHONE 01-937 4677 (answering service)

A Regency rosewood cabinet, probably by Louis Le Gaigneur. Circa 1815.
See *English Furniture, the Georgian period 1750–1830* by Jourdain and Rose, page 150.

O. F. Wilson Limited

Queen's Elm Parade, Old Church Street, London sw3 6ej

TELEPHONE 01-352 9554

Pair of Louis XV bergères in beech. 1750.
Louis XVI painted console table with shaped breccia marble top. 1780.
Six-fold painted canvas screen. French, early 19th century. Height 198 cm (6 ft 6 in).
Pair of Louis XV ormolu candlesticks. 1760.
Louis XVI white marble ormolu mounted clock. 1780.

Christopher Wood Gallery

15 Motcomb Street, Belgravia, London SW1X 8LB
TELEPHONE 01-235 9141/2

The Entrance to an Old Timbered House,
by Samuel Dukinfield Swarbreck.
Signed and dated 1853. Oil on canvas.
77.5 × 63.5 cm (30½ × 25 in).

Harriet Wynter Limited (Arts & Sciences)

50 Redcliffe Road, London SW10 9NJ

TELEPHONE 01-352 6494

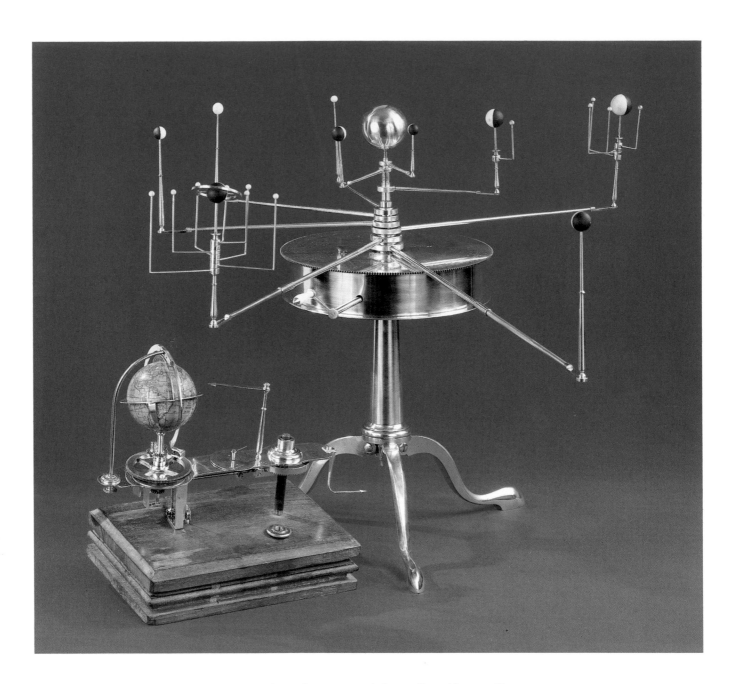

Martin-type planetarium or orrery in brass, silvered brass and ivory.
Signed "T. BLUNT", the movement signed "GEORGE NEWMAN FECIT, Dec. 1808",
countersigned "THOS VOIGT".
English, with American repairs, early 19th century.
With alternative Tellurion unit.
The calendar plate is 22 cm (8¾ in) in diameter.

Maurice Asprey Limited

41 Duke Street, St. James's, London SW1Y 6DF

TELEPHONE 01-930 3921

A selection of antique jewellery and objets de vertu.

Bobinet

102 Mount Street, London W1YD 5HF

TELEPHONE 01-408 0333/4

A German quarter-striking table clock with alarm and dials
on all four sides, with its original four-train steel movement.
Circa 1570. Height 21.6 cm (8½ in).

Crawley and Asquith Limited
Fine Arts
16 Savile Row, London WIX IAE
TELEPHONE 01-930 0138

A Study from Nature
by John Frederick Herring Jnr. (fl. 1860–75).
Oil on canvas; signed, inscribed and dated 1867.
61 × 106.7 cm (24 × 42 in).

Ronald A. Lee (Fine Arts) Limited

1–9 Bruton Place, London WIX 7AD
TELEPHONE 01-629 5600/01-499 6266

A most noble and hitherto unrecorded Charles II
walnut longcase clock by Joseph Knibb,
London, with a four-quarter striking movement
of month duration.

Ronald A. Lee plc

1–9 Bruton Place, London W1X 7AD

TELEPHONE 01-629 5600/01-499 6266

A George II mahogany bookcase with broken pediment and cornice; the lower part with pagoda mouldings, the drawers and plinth decorated with blind fretwork. Circa 1755.
Height 256.5 cm (8 ft 5 in) Width 223.5 cm (7 ft 4 in).
See: *The Dictionary of English Furniture* by MacQuoid and Edwards, 1926, vol. I, page 77, fig. 19.

D. M. & P. Manheim (Peter Manheim) Limited

69 Upper Berkeley Street, Portman Square, London W1H 7DH
TELEPHONE 01-723 6595

Chelsea Porcelain leaf dish. Red Anchor mark. Circa 1755. Length 24 cm (9½ in).
A pair of elegant Bow Porcelain figures of fruit sellers with their animals.
Anchor and Dagger marks in red.
Circa 1760. Height 21.6 cm (8½ in).
Very rare salt-glaze Staffordshire pottery jug and cover. Painted with a scene of Cupid and a young girl in
a large heart-shaped panel. Smaller panels with bow and arrow, quiver etc. Intended as a love gift.
Circa 1760. Height 14 cm (5½ in).

Steppes Hill Farm Antiques

The Hill Farm, Stockbury, Sittingbourne, Kent ME9 7RB
TELEPHONE 0795 842205

A fine and rare Chelsea Raised Anchor beaker, circa 1748.
Painted with a Ho-Ho bird under a chocolate line border to the rim,
after the Kakiemon original.
A similar example from the Triangle period is in
The Colonial Williamsburg Foundation, Virginia, U.S.A.

Anthony Woodburn Limited

Orchard House, High Street, Leigh, Tonbridge, Kent TN11 8RH

TELEPHONE 0732 832258

Important walnut veneered longcase clock by George Graham, London. Circa 1730.

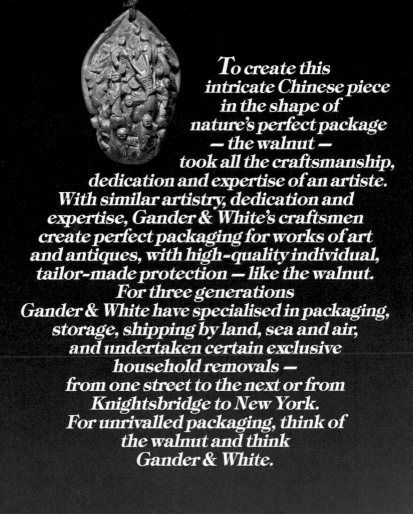

*To create this
intricate Chinese piece
in the shape of
nature's perfect package
— the walnut —
took all the craftsmanship,
dedication and expertise of an artiste.
With similar artistry, dedication and
expertise, Gander & White's craftsmen
create perfect packaging for works of art
and antiques, with high-quality individual,
tailor-made protection — like the walnut.
For three generations
Gander & White have specialised in packaging,
storage, shipping by land, sea and air,
and undertaken certain exclusive
household removals —
from one street to the next or from
Knightsbridge to New York.
For unrivalled packaging, think of
the walnut and think
Gander & White.*

Gander & White

*21 Lillie Road, London SW6 1UE.
Tel: 01-381 0571
159 East 63rd Street, New York 10021.
Tel: (212) 888 1839*

Our thanks to Norman Adams and Colefax & Fowler for their help with our stand.

After shipping the Treasure Houses of Britain Exhibition, we're ready to handle <u>your</u> shipment.

Packing and shipping to Washington DC the majority of loans for the Treasure Houses of Britain Exhibition was a mammoth undertaking – by any standards.

That Pitt & Scott were chosen as principal shippers, says everything for our skills, experience and impeccable reputation.

Your own requirements may be a little less demanding! Nevertheless, we believe your consignment deserves just as much care. Good reason for entrusting the job to Pitt & Scott.

This means that you will benefit from the packing and handling skills we bring to shipping priceless works of art.

What's more, you will be able to rely on our faultless organisation – the knowledge and experience gained during over a century of operation.

We take care of *everything* involved, including customs, warehousing at either end, even your personal travel arrangements.

Like the Treasure Houses of Britain, you'll be in safe hands with Pitt & Scott.

Packing at Chatsworth before shipment to Washington DC.

Pitt & Scott
In safe hands

20/24 Eden Grove, Holloway Rd, London N7 8ED
Tel: 01-607 7321 Telex: 21857

Non-Exhibitors

JEREMY LTD

255 KING'S ROAD, CHELSEA, LONDON SW3
Tel: 01-352 0644, 01-352 3127   Cables: Jeremique, London SW3

**A HIGHLY IMPORTANT ENGLISH CHIPPENDALE PERIOD CARVED
WOOD AND GILDED WALL MIRROR**
Date circa 1765
Height 58″ 1 m 48 cms   Width 28½″ 73 cms

JEREMY LTD

255 KING'S ROAD, CHELSEA, LONDON SW3
Tel: 01-352 0644, 01-352 3127   Cables: Jeremique, London SW3

A SUPERB QUALITY ENGLISH EARLY REGENCY PERIOD ROSEWOOD ROLL TOP
WRITING DESK WITH ORIGINAL BRASS MOUNTS
Date circa 1805
Height 53″ 135 cms   Width 32″ 81.5 cms   Depth 19½″ 49.5 cms

EMPEROR OF THE FRENCH, LEGAL REFORMER, MILITARY GENIUS AND OUR 1,643RD CLIENT.

When Napoleon had made his last charge, one Harry Phillips of London was charged with disposing of the emperor's assets.

Not that such an auction was particularly unusual for our founder.

Indeed, twenty-five years earlier, after the revolutionaries had brought down the blade on the head of Marie Antoinette, it was Mr Phillips who brought down the gavel on her collection of paintings.

However illustrious our past client list may be, Phillips today prides itself on being accessible to everyone, whether they bring us a fine work of art or a merely functional piece of furniture.

Everyone who comes to Phillips can have personal contact with any of one-hundred-and-twenty or so specialists, a decided advantage, as regular vendors at auction will know.

And with eighteen auction

rooms throughout the country, by far the largest network in the UK, the specialists are always available for you to call upon.

If you would like any further information about Phillips, as well as a complimentary copy of our preview of forthcoming auctions, just ring Andrew Singleton on 01-629 6602.

You'll find our service as impressive as our heritage.

F I N E   A R T
A U C T I O N E E R S
A N D   V A L U E R S
S I N C E   1 7 9 6

BLENSTOCK HOUSE, 7 BLENHEIM STREET, NEW BOND STREET, LONDON W1Y 0AS · Telephone: 01-629 6602
LONDON (3 AUCTION ROOMS) · BATH · CAMBRIDGE · CARDIFF · CHESTER · COLWYN BAY · CORNWALL · EDINBURGH · EXETER · FOLKESTONE
GLASGOW · IPSWICH · KNOWLE · LEEDS · MELBOURNE · MORLEY · NORWICH · OXFORD · SHERBORNE · BRUSSELS · GENEVA · NEW YORK · PARIS · ZURICH
Members of the Society of Fine Art Auctioneers.

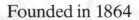

Bernheimer

Founded in 1864

An important Chinese Rouleau Vase. K'ang-Hsi (1662-1722). Porcelain, painted in the colours of the "famille verte", the long neck decorated with a frieze of lambrequins and various stylized ornaments, the shoulders with cartouches depicting precious objects, and the body richly embellished with a lacustre landscape, pavilions and figures.
Height: 78cms.

Compare: a similar example of this rare type illustrated in: Walter Bondy, K'ang-Hsi, München 1923, plate 140. Another example is to be found in the Metropolitan Museum of Art, New York, illustrated in: Oriental Ceramics, The World's Great Collections, Vol. 12, The Metropolitan Museum of Art, Kodansha, Tokyo 1977, plate 131.

BERNHEIMER FINE ARTS LTD, 32 ST. GEORGE STREET, LONDON W1R 9FA, TEL: 01-499 0293, TELEX: 268091.

Bernheimer
Founded in 1864

Louis XVI Secrétaire à Abattant, stamped C. Topino JME (Charles Topino, Maître 1773).
Oak, richly inlaid with rosewood, kingwood and others in a flower marquetry and a top of Brescia marble.
Height: 129cms, Width: 76.5cms, Depth: 39cms.
Provenance: Collection W.S. Broadwood.

Compare: Jean Nicolay, L'Art et la Manière des Maîtres Ebénistes Français au XVIII Siècle, Paris 1976, p.465. figs Z. and Y.

L. BERNHEIMER KG, LENBACHPLATZ 3, 8000 MÜNCHEN 2, TEL: 089-59 66 43. TELEX: 5 212 724

MALLETT

BY APPOINTMENT TO THE LATE QUEEN MARY

A very rare Queen Anne cream lacquer bracket clock by Joseph Windmills, London, circa 1710.
Height: 26 ins.   Width: 15 ins.   Depth: 8½ ins.

MALLETT & SON (ANTIQUES) LTD., 40 NEW BOND STREET, LONDON W1Y 0BS. TELEPHONE: 01-499 7411 (5 lines)
TELEX 25692 CABLES: MALLETSON LONDON W1Y 0BS and at BOURDON HOUSE, 2 DAVIES STREET, LONDON W1Y 1LJ

TZIGANY
– FINE ARTS –

Antoine Chenevière

28, 29 DOVER STREET, LONDON W1X 3PA
Tel: (01) 491 1007   Telex: Tzigan 262 105

Russian, Austrian, Italian and German 18th- and 19th-century furniture and Objets d'art

An important Russian vase in a mosaic of Urals Malachite. Czar Nicholas I. Circa 1835, set on a late 18th-century Russian column in mahogany and brass.

Late 18th-century Russian chairs in mahogany and brass, two of a set of four designed by Heinreich Gambs 1765–1831.

A.D.C. Heritage Limited

Dealers in Antique Silver

18th Century Silver for 20th Century Living

2 Old Bond Street London W1X 3TD Tel: 01-493 5088

LUCY B. CAMPBELL · GEORGINA FINE ARTS

1 HANS PLACE, LONDON SW1X 0EU
Telephone 01-589 4295 or 01-584 7990

17th–19th-CENTURY
DECORATIVE PRINTS

PRÉVOST, JEAN-LOUIS
Published Paris, circa 1803

PELHAM GALLERIES

163 & 165 Fulham Road London sw3 6sn
telephones 01-589 2686 & 2692

A pair of large amphora shaped vases
The scenes depict the tombs of Plinius and Archimedes and are almost certainly the work of
W.L. Stier who was involved in the Plinius reconstructions at Tuscum in 1832.
The reverse sides are decorated with floral sprays.
Berlin K.P.M., circa 1837.
26½" (67cm) high

A Russian 36 light chandelier in gilt brass
*Designed by Rossi and executed by the Kitner workshops, it compares closely to one
in Pavlovsk.
St Petersburg, circa 1815.
52″ (132cm) drop, 50″ (127cm) width*

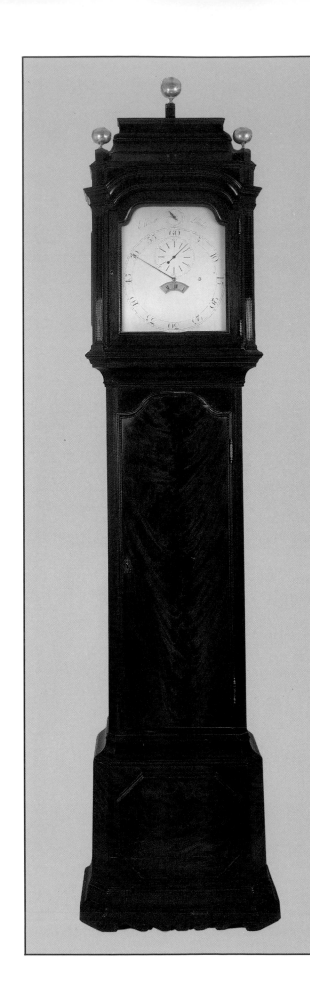

A very important George II mahogany
regulator of month duration by
John Ellicott, *F.R.S.*
The clock is in fine original state and
incorporates his compensating pendulum.

John Carlton Smith
&
Terence Camerer Cuss
17 Ryder Street, St. James's, London SW1Y 6PY
Telephone 01-930 6622 and 01-930 1941

POLAK
EST 1854

FINE 19th AND 20th CENTURY PAINTINGS
AND WATERCOLOURS

William Duffield 1816–1863

Still life of black cock, wood pigeon, a stein,
a silver gilt claret jug and fruit on a marble ledge

Signed and dated 1855

On canvas – 28 by 36 inches

21 King Street, St. James's, London SW1Y 6QY
Telephone: 01-839 2871/2   Telex: 885991 Hyde G

RONALD PHILLIPS LTD

An extremely rare Regency carved giltwood oval jardiniere with a motif of acanthus leaves to the shaped body, centred by a grotesque mask and supported by two winged gryphons; on an oval marbleised base.
Circa 1810
Height 40in (102cm) Width 30in (76cm) Depth 19in (48cm)

26 BRUTON STREET, LONDON, W1X 8LH

Telephone: 01-493 2341

RONALD PHILLIPS LTD

A fine George II walnut mirror with gilt mouldings,
foliated pendants and broken swan-neck pediment centred by an eagle.
Circa 1745
Height 54in (137cm) Width 26in (66cm)

26 BRUTON STREET, LONDON, W1X 8LH

Telephone: 01-493 2341

John Nost Sartorius, *The Old Surrey stag hounds with the stag being released to the left, the field standing to the centre, and the hounds to the right*, oil on canvas, 94 by 139 cm. (37 by 54½ in.). Estimate: £20,000-30,000. To be included in our sale of Important British Paintings 1500-1850, 15th July.

Important Summer Auctions

19th Century Decorative Art 11th and 12th June
Indian, Himalayan and South-East Asian Works of Art 15th June
Fine Japanese Works of Art 17th and 18th June
Important English Silver 18th June
Illustrated and Private Press Books, Childrens' Books and Related Drawings 18th and 19th June
Continental Pottery and Porcelain 23rd June
Instruments of Science and Technology 23rd June
Western Manuscripts and Miniatures 23rd June
19th Century European Paintings, Drawings and Watercolours 23rd to 25th June
Important French Furniture 26th June
Important Tribal Art 29th June
Important Old Master, Decorative, 19th and 20th Century Prints 29th and 30th June
Impressionist, Modern and Contemporary Art 30th June to 2nd July
Old Master Paintings 8th July
European Works of Art and Sculpture 9th July
Fine Jewels and Jewels for the Collector 9th July
Important English Furniture 10th and 17th July
English and Continental Glass 13th July
Antiquities 13th and 14th July
English Naive and Provincial Art 13th and 14th July
Important British Paintings 1500-1850 15th July
English Literature and History: Books and Manuscripts 23rd and 24th July

34-35 New Bond Street, London W1A 2AA. Telephone: (01) 493 8080. Telex: 24454 SPBLON G.

SOTHEBY'S

FOUNDED 1744

de havilland (antiques) ltd

48 Sloane Street   London SW1X 9LU   01-235 3534

A magnificent Dutch walnut longcase clock with gilt enrichments, Dutch strike, day, date, signs of the Zodiac and phases of the moon, maker Jan Breukelaar, date, second quarter of the 18th century. Height 9′ 2″

de havilland (antiques) ltd

48 Sloane Street   London SW1X 9LU   01-235 3534

A small and rare Queen Anne walnut bureau cabinet, single domed, with brushing slide above four long drawers, handles later.
Height 5' 4",
Width 1' 7½",
Depth 1' 1½"

JACK CASIMIR LTD

SPECIALISTS IN ANTIQUE METALWARE

23 PEMBRIDGE ROAD · LONDON W11 3HG · ENGLAND
TELEPHONE : 01 · 727 8643

*A selection of English and European candlesticks
in brass and bronze dating from 1500 to 1660.*

We maintain an extremely large and varied selection
of fine 16th. to 19th. Century English and Continental
brass, copper, bronze and pewter.

H. C. Baxter & Sons

PARTNERS: R. C. BAXTER · T. J. BAXTER · M. K. BAXTER · J. BAXTER · G. J. BAXTER

SPECIALISTS IN 18TH CENTURY FURNITURE

A Regency brass inlaid mahogany breakfront bookcase, c.1810.
Length 5'   Depth 1' 3"   Height 3' 2"

TELEPHONE : 01-352 9826 0807

191/193/195 FULHAM ROAD
SOUTH KENSINGTON · SW3 6JL

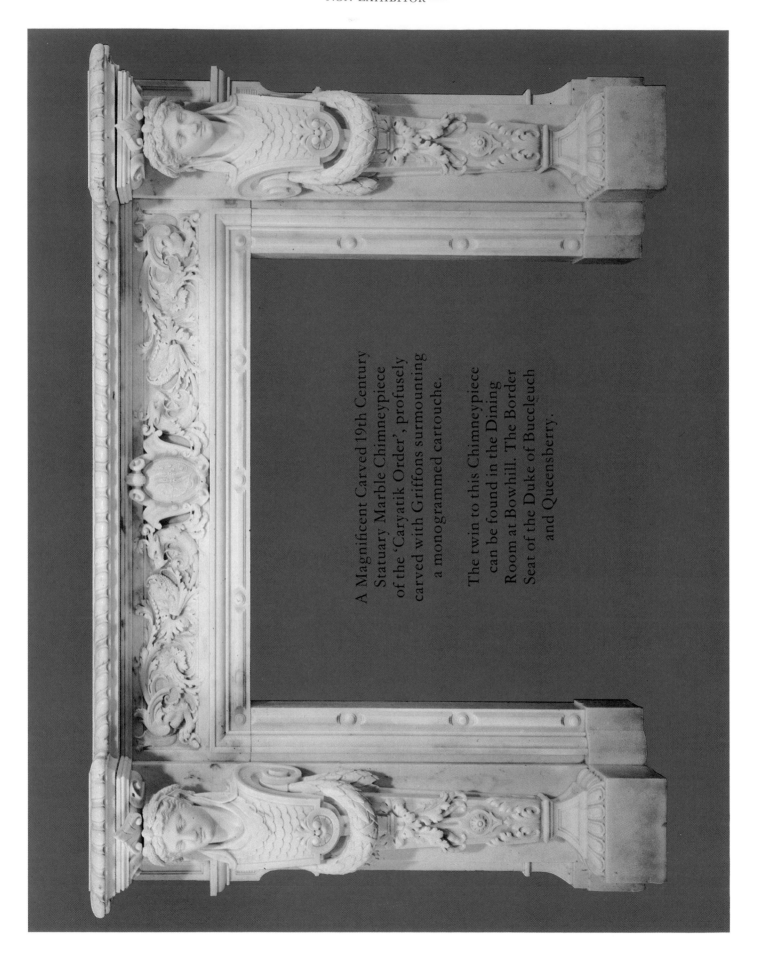

A Magnificent Carved 19th Century
Statuary Marble Chimneypiece
of the 'Caryatik Order', profusely
carved with Griffons surmounting
a monogrammed cartouche.

The twin to this Chimneypiece
can be found in the Dining
Room at Bowhill. The Border
Seat of the Duke of Buccleuch
and Queensberry.

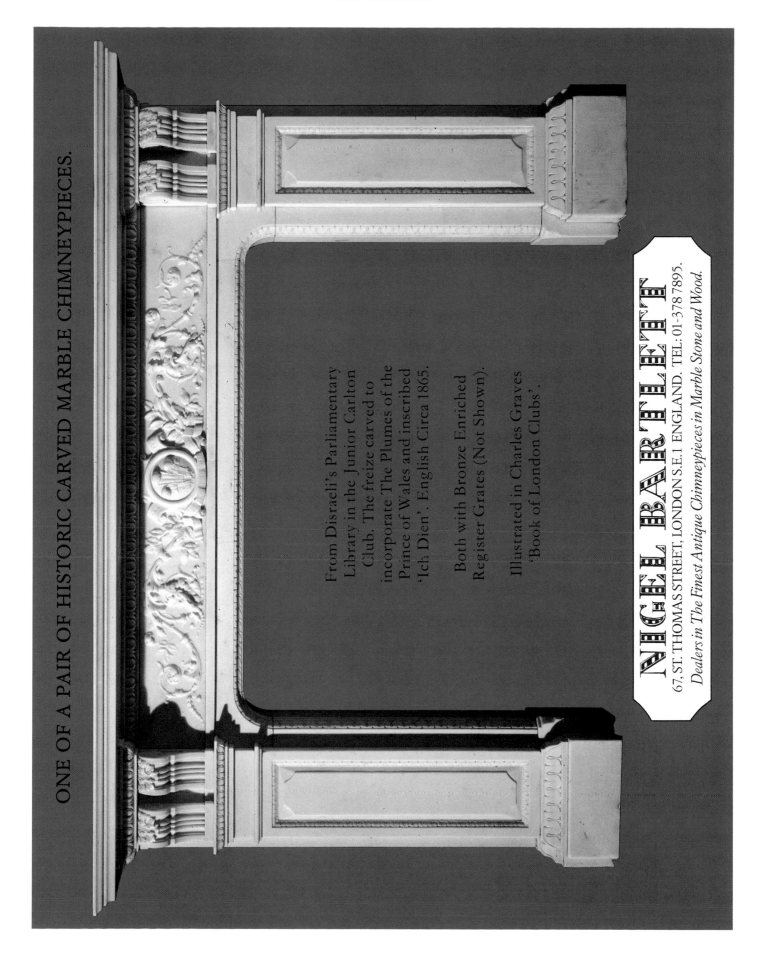

ONE OF A PAIR OF HISTORIC CARVED MARBLE CHIMNEYPIECES.

From Disraeli's Parliamentary Library in the Junior Carlton Club. The freize carved to incorporate The Plumes of the Prince of Wales and inscribed 'Ich Dien'. English Circa 1865.

Both with Bronze Enriched Register Grates (Not Shown).

Illustrated in Charles Graves 'Book of London Clubs'.

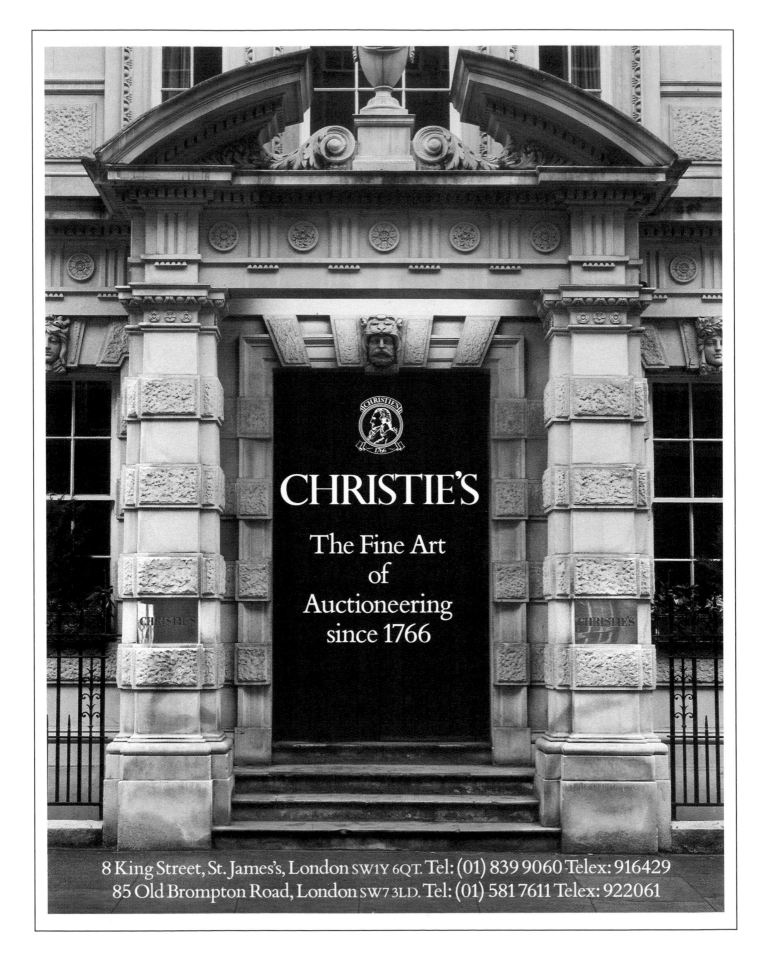

FRANCE

néGocIants en objets d'art,
tableaux anciens et modernes

11, rue Jean-Mermoz – 75008 PARIS – Tél.: (1)42 25 44 33

The XIVe Biennale Internationale des Antiquaires
at the Grand Palais in Paris is already in preparation.

Collectors, Amateurs and Dealers will be interested
to know that it will be held in 1988
from September 22nd to October 10th.

The catalogue of the XIII Biennale is still available.

*These two emblems offer security. Their holders provide
collectors with all desirable guarantees for purchases as well as
sales, valuations and divisions. Each subject sold by them is
guaranteed in writing to be from the period it is represented to be.*

J. & M. Wolber

Savonnerie
(détail)
Époque Louis XVI c 1775
8,20 m × 6,10 m
(23 ft × 20 ft)

YVES MIKAELOFF

Meubles, Tapis et Tapisseries de Rois

10 et 14 rue Royale   75008 Paris - FRANCE

Tél. (1) 42.61.64.42

J. & M. Wolber

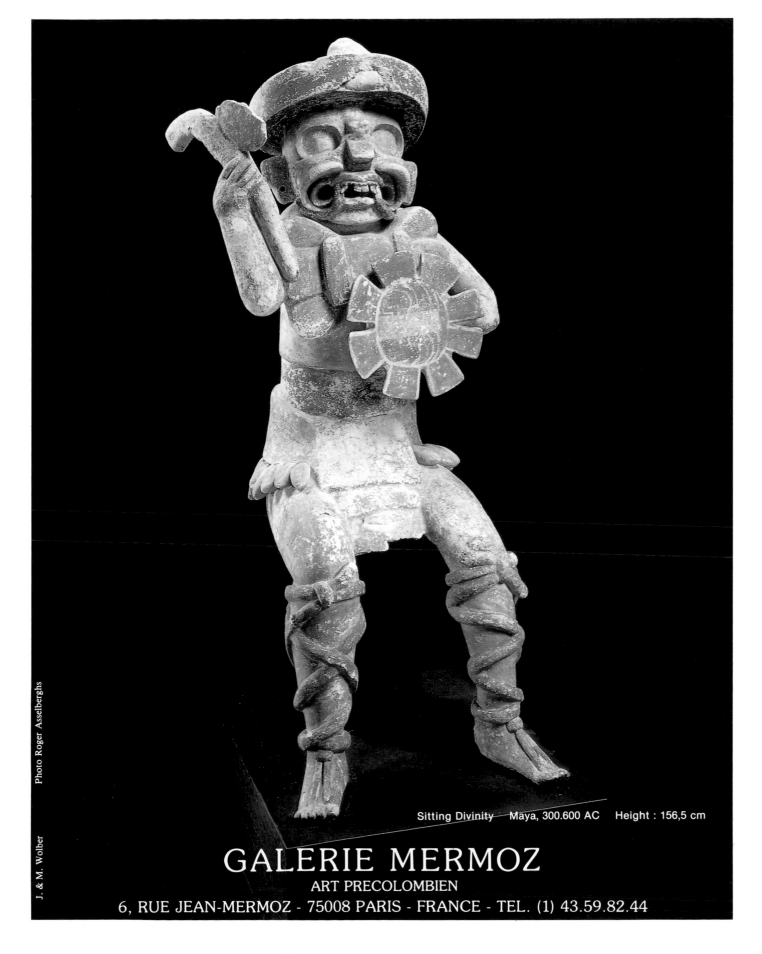

Sitting Divinity   Maya, 300.600 AC   Height : 156,5 cm

GALERIE MERMOZ
ART PRECOLOMBIEN
6, RUE JEAN-MERMOZ - 75008 PARIS - FRANCE - TEL. (1) 43.59.82.44

JACQUES BARRERE

ART D'EXTRÊME ORIENT

36, rue Mazarine 75006 PARIS France
Tél. (1) 43 26 57 61

J. & M. Wolber

A GROUP
OF CHINESE POTTERY FIGURES AND JARS
DATED FROM THE NEOLITHIC TO THE WEI

BRAME & LORENCEAU

Tableaux - Dessins - Sculptures - de 1820 à 1920

68, boulevard Malesherbes 75008 Paris France
tél. : (1) 45.22.16.89

Edgar Degas 1834–1917
"Danseuse sur la Scène"
Dessin au fusain rehaussé de pastel vers 1885
Cachet de la Vente Degas en bas à gauche
Inscription de la main de Degas en haut à droite :
"bon port, la tête un peu tournée sur la gauche"
Hauteur 0,30 m. 11¾″   Largeur 0,23 m. 9″

ARIANE DANDOIS

61, RUE DES SAINTS-PERES 75006 PARIS FRANCE   **TELEPHONE: (1) 42 22 14 43**

J. & M. Wolber

A set of four Regency mahogany urns with bronze mounts, on stands.
Height urns: 36 inches   Height base: 51 inches

ÉMILE BOURGEY

NUMISMATIQUE

7, RUE DROUOT 75009 PARIS FRANCE
TEL (1) 47 70 88 67-47 70 35 18

Among the "twelve Caesars" (Suetonius): "Aurei" with portraits in high relief of Tiberius (A.D. 14–37), Claudius (A.D. 41–54), Nero (A.D. 54–68), Titus (A.D. 79–81) and Domitian (A.D. 81–96).
The most beautiful coins of the Roman Empire . . .

Emile Bourgey – Sabine Bourgey, Experts

ON THE LEFT BANK OF THE SEINE FACING THE LOUVRE

GALERIE CAMOIN

9, QUAI VOLTAIRE 75007 PARIS Tél. (1) 42.61.82.06

Console side-table in amboina burl
attributed to Adam Weisweiler, master in 1778.
White and grey marble top.
Wide rectangular dark blue Wedgwood plate decorated with white biscuit,
marked with the monogram I, moulded after a drawing by Lady Templetown.
Galleried tray. Four top-shaped feet.
H.96cm-37¾″ - W.1,65m-65″ - D.52cm-20½″

J. & M. Wolber

J.O. LEEGENHOEK

FINE OLD MASTER PAINTINGS

Frans SNYDERS (1579-1657)

A still life of fruits in a basket

Panel 58,3 × 82,7 cm

The reverse of the panel bears the marks of Saint Luc's Guild, Antwerp, as well as the initials of the panel maker, Michiel Vriendt, who became a master in 1615 and died in 1636.

This painting is a relatively early work, which shows stylistic similarities with other works painted during the years 1610-1616.

23 quai Voltaire 75007 PARIS - FRANCE - tél. (1) 42.96.36.08

CHARLES RATTON & GUY LADRIÈRE

ANTIQUE - MOYEN ÂGE - ARTS PRIMITIFS
TABLEAUX - OBJETS D'ART

Bronze - Italy 16th Century
Height: 24 cm

J. & M. Wolber

14, rue de Marignan, 75008 Paris France. Tél. (1) 43.59.58.21

23, rue de Beaune, 75007 Paris France. Tél. (1) 42.61.09.57

GERARD FLEURY

PRECIOUS AND RARE BOOKS

First editions – Literature – Bindings – Manuscripts (illuminated) – Hunting

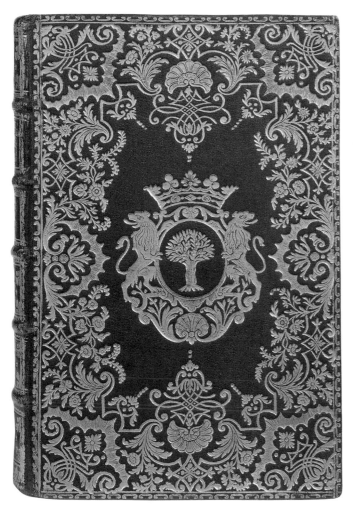

ALMANACH ROYAL 1764
Contemporary red morocco eighteenth Century,
in the finest condition, with Dubuisson's dentelle,
and arms of Earl of Riocour. In-8

GEORGES BRAQUE'S LITHOGRAPHIES
Lettera Amorosa. 1963

One of the most sumptuous illustrated modern books,
with a wonderful binding by P. L. MARTIN. In-quarto

46, RUE PIERRE CHARRON – 75008 PARIS – FRANCE – Tel. (1) 47.20.42.67

Extensively illustrated colour catalogue available £15 (postage and packing included).
For any researches and advice write to Gérard FLEURY.

ROBERT DICKSON ANTIQUES LTD.

263 FULHAM ROAD
LONDON SW3 6HY
01-351 0330

Fine Chippendale Mahogany Serving Table, circa 1760
Pair of early 19th-century marble Urns
Pair of Sheraton painted Elbow Chairs
Late 18th-century French tôle Tray
Pair mid-19th-century Chinese Silk Pictures
Pair French Empire bronze Lions
Early 19th-century Italian marble Bath

ANTHONY JAMES & SON LTD.

LONDON

NEW YORK

88 Fulham Road · London SW3 · 01-584 1120

GRIMALDI

Twelve Royal Arcade
Old Bond Street, London, W1X 3HB
01-493 3953

A finely preserved English Carriage Clock with outer travelling case.
James McCabe London Circa 1860

We stock an interesting and varied selection of
clocks, barometers, scientific instruments, wrist watches and pocket watches
from around the world

IN ASSOCIATION WITH ANTIQUORUM
GENEVA · LONDON · NEW YORK · HONG KONG

not everything worth looking at in London is here at Grosvenor House…

BONHAMS THE KNIGHTSBRIDGE AUCTIONEERS

William Thompson: 'A King Charles Spaniel in a Landscape' (detail)

In 1793, Bonhams opened their first Gallery. Nearly two hundred years later, Bonhams is still very much a family firm, offering the high standard of personal service and expertise that you would expect from a family company approaching its two-hundredth anniversary.

Situated in Knightsbridge two minutes' walk from the west side of Harrods, Bonhams holds up to seven auctions a week with late night viewing on Tuesdays.

Each month there are oil painting, silver, furniture, jewellery, watercolour and ceramics sales.

In addition regular sales are held of carpets, modern paintings, clocks, prints and books.

Specialist 'Theme' Sales are also held to coincide with major exhibitions and shows in London. At these auctions up to 700 lots of paintings, ceramics and works of art all with a related subject are on view. These include the Boat Show in January, Crufts in February, Chelsea Flower Show in May, Royal Ascot in June, Cowes Week in August and Smithfield in December.

For further information on Bonhams and details of forthcoming sales please contact Sophie Brookes.

BONHAMS, FINE ART AUCTIONEERS & VALUERS,
MONTPELIER GALLERIES, MONTPELIER STREET, LONDON SW7 1HH. Tel: 01-584 9161.

WILLIAM BEDFORD
PERIOD FURNITURE AND WORKS OF ART

William Bedford PLC
The Merchants Hall 46 Essex Road London N1 8LN
Telephone 01-226 9648

A fine Regency period rosewood centre table with carved acanthus decoration,
parcel-gilded details and original specimen marble top
Circa 1815   *Provenance:* Sheringham Hall

WITNEY ANTIQUES
(L.S.A. & C.J. JARRETT)
96–98 CORN STREET, WITNEY, OXON OX8 7BU
Tel: Witney (0993) 3902

A highly important enclosed chest of drawers that can be assigned to the reign of Charles I. Dated 1647 this interesting cabinet of architectural construction, in Oak, has decorative veneers of Snakewood and Ebony inlaid with floral design in Ivory and Mother of Pearl. The doors with scrolled pediments surmount an architrave enclosing arches in perspective. A scarcity exists of English Cabinets that can be dated prior to 1650 and directly reflect the influence of Inigo Jones who died in 1652.

PROVENANCE AVAILABLE

Ref: Illustrated in the *Dictionary of English Furniture*, and the subject of an article in *Country Life*, 7th Dec 1918

Raffety

34 Kensington Church Street, London W8 4HA

TELEPHONE 01-938 1100

HENRY JONES, LONDON

An early and rare ebony striking table clock signed at the base of the dial
Henricus Jones in the Temple Fecit.
Date Circa 1670. Height 42.5 cm (16¾ in).
This clock represents one of a select group of important seventeenth and
eighteenth-century clocks and barometers, currently available.
Each piece is accompanied by a documented statement detailing its state of preservation,
provenance, if known, and history of the maker

Christopher Bangs

by appointment only

**Early metalware and metalwork
and works of art
01-223 5676**

BRASS CANDLESTICKS 1450–1750
a selection of pieces recently bought and sold by us

Harvey Ferry · William Clegg

The Barns · 1 High St · Nettlebed

Oxfordshire RG9 5AA

Tel: 0491 641533

JOHN BARRY

BARTON END HALL,
Near NAILSWORTH, GLOUCESTERSHIRE, GL6 0QQ

1 mile south of Nailsworth on the A46 Bath Road
Telephone Nailsworth (045 383) 3471

A small pair of Regency period rosewood chiffoniers, circa 1815
Height: 118cm (46½in)   Width 71cm (28in)   Depth 33cm (13in)

Fine 18th and early 19th century English and
Continental Furniture, Paintings and Objects of Art.

Open Monday to Saturday 10am to 5·30pm or by appointment.

Nigel Milne Ltd.

16c Grafton Street London W1.   Tel 01-493 9646

CIRENCESTER ANTIQUES LTD

Established in the Cotswolds for 30 years

An exceptionally well drawn mid 18th century oak chest on stand
77″ high, 44″ wide, 26″ deep.

1½ hours by M4 or M40 motorways

17 DYER STREET CIRENCESTER GLOS GL7 2PP

Telephone Cirencester (0285) 2955   Private car park at rear of premises

GEORGE JOHNSON (ANTIQUES)

17th & 18th Century English Furniture

120 Kensington Park Road, London W11 2PW

Telephone: 01-229 3119

Member of the Kensington and Chelsea Chamber of Commerce

George III mahogany and brass bound oval wine-cooler
30" wide, 21" deep and 26" high
English, circa 1780

Cambridge Fine Art

Fine British and Continental Paintings, 1700–1940

'Sunset – Feeding Sheep' by John Linnell (1792–1882)
Oil on panel, 70 × 99 cm (27½ × 39 in)
Signed and dated 1863
Exhibited: Royal Academy 1863, No 671
Royal Academy 1883, 'Exhibition of Old Masters', No. 83
Royal Academy 1901, Winter Exhibition, No. 9
Provenance: H. J. Turner Esq, Stockleigh House, Regents Park

Priesthouse
33 Church Street
Little Shelford
Cambridge CB2 5HG

Tel 0223-842866
0223-843537
By appointment

EXHIBITING:
The Fine Art and Antiques Fair, Olympia, London, 5th to 14th June 1987, Stand No 16 (Gold Section).

MILLERS ANTIQUES KELVEDON

One of a pair of 18th-century Tea Tables

46 High Street, Kelvedon, Essex, England
Telephone Kelvedon (0376) 70098. Telex 987562

Specialists in 17th-, 18th- & 19th-century English and French Furniture

One of the largest stocks of Antique Furniture in Essex.

Huntington Antiques Ltd.

Early Period Furniture, Works of Art & Tapestries.
Fine Country Furniture, Metalware, Treen & Textiles.
The Old Forge, Church Street, Stow-on-the-Wold, Gloucestershire. Tel: 0451 30842.

A glorious late medieval oak livery cupboard in complete state. . . Northern European
or possibly English, circa 1525.

John Muir, Collectors Guide, February 1987

**We offer a substantial stock of fine early oak, walnut and country furniture. Always a
selection of refectory, gateleg and other tables; dressers and court cupboards; wainscots
and sets of chairs; and usually some rare examples of Gothic and Renaissance furniture.
We would always welcome the opportunity to purchase such items.**

Open Mon–Sat 9–6 and by appointment

Established 1926

Omnia Vincit Veritas

ART AND ANTIQUE DEALERS LEAGUE OF AMERICA, INC.

The Art and Antique Dealers League of America, Inc., is the oldest and principal antiques and fine arts organization in America. It is an outgrowth of the Antique Dealers Luncheon Club, which on January 7, 1926 met at the Madison Hotel in New York City and formed the Antique and Decorative Arts League. In 1942, "to give the organization a wider ramification in every phase of the arts", the name was changed to the Art and Antique Dealers League of America, Inc.

The purpose in forming the League was to bring the various members of the art and antiques trade closer together to promote a greater understanding among themselves and with the public, and generally to devote itself to the best interests of dealers and collectors of antiques and works of art.

The late James P. Montllor, an expert in Spanish art, was the primary mover behind the organization at its inception and throughout its early years. The first president was the noted collector and dealer, Charles J. Duveen.

The League is one of the founders of C.I.N.O.A. (Confédération Internationale des Négociants en Oeuvres d'Art), which is an international organization of European and American dealers. Each year the League contributes to the granting of a prize to a student for study, research and the publishing of articles and books on antiques and fine art.

The League is strict in its standards for accepting members. Each applicant must be an established dealer whose art objects are of the highest quality. Each member subscribes to and strictly observes the League's Code of Ethics. This code determines the manner in which the dealer conducts his business so as to command the respect and confidence of his clients. All invoices or memorandums of sales must contain a fair description of the articles sold, the date or origin, the maker, if known, and condition or repairs. Any member who does not adhere strictly to the Code of Ethics is expelled from the League. Members shall, in all their dealings with the public and with their fellow members, adhere to moral and ethical standards of conduct. This is of utmost importance in the realm of antiques and fine art, where the public deals with experts upon whose judgment it must rely.

To purchase antiques or fine art with absolute confidence, look for the blue and gold plaque and Member Certificate of the *Art and Antique Dealers League of America*. A brochure with the names and addresses of each member listing their specialties is available at no charge. If you would like to receive the current edition, please write: Art and Antique Dealers League of America, Inc., 353 East 78th Street, New York, New York 10021.

STAIR & CO.

ESTABLISHED 1912 NEW YORK

A rare George III serpentine mahogany commode. English, circa 1760
Size: 36″ wide 20½″ deep 33½″ high

942 MADISON AVENUE, NEW YORK N.Y. 10021 • 517-4400

OXFORD ANTIQUE RESTORERS LTD. • (212) 355-7620

120 MOUNT STREET, LONDON W1Y 5HB • 01-499 1784

Place des Antiquaires

125 EAST 57th STREET, NEW YORK CITY • (212) 355-0500

The Center Of The World

90 Antiques Dealers

A Chippendale Carved
Giltwood Overmantel
Mirror, Circa 1770.
Width: 71"   Height: 53"

Made by
Thomas Chippendale,
the Younger,
for Harewood House
from a design
by Robert Adam.

Hyde Park Antiques, Ltd.

836 Broadway (at 13th Street) ∽ New York, N.Y. 10003 ∽ (212) 477-0033

Finest English Antique Furniture

LAWRENCE BRASS & SON
Conservation and Restoration of fine Antiques

We restore good quality Antique Furniture and objects with emphasis on early oak and walnut, decorated, lacquer and gilt items.

We restore for both private and trade customers as well as maintaining important private and institutional collections.

We have restored furniture from collections including the Sherwood and Fardon collections, and leading museums, including the V & A.

Our specialists offer you a comprehensive service which includes –

● Upholstery to traditional standards ● Marble restoration ● Metal restoration
● Casting of mounts, handles etc. in yellow brass, bronze and precious metals ● Water and oil gilding
● Fire gilding ● Carving ● Ornamental turning ● Ivory inlay and engraving ● Leather tops

For enquiries please ring

In the West Country,
Bath (0225) 64057

In London,
01-636 3401

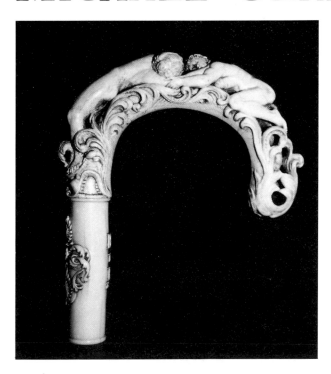

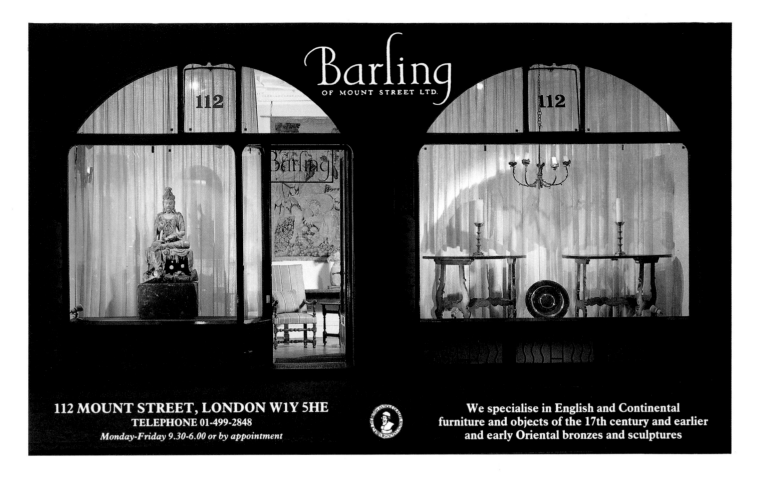
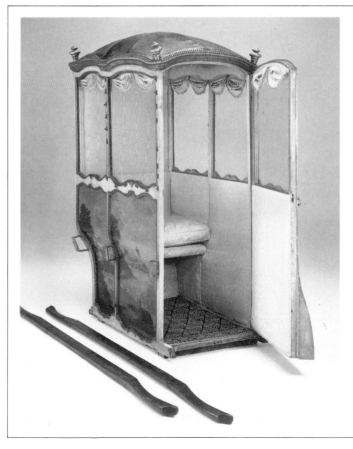

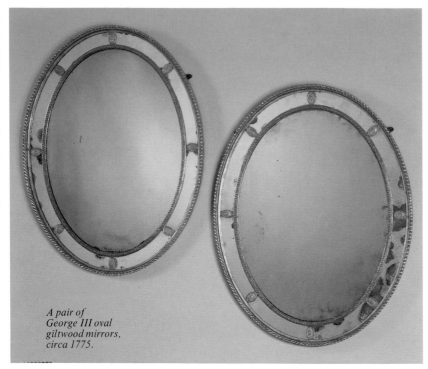

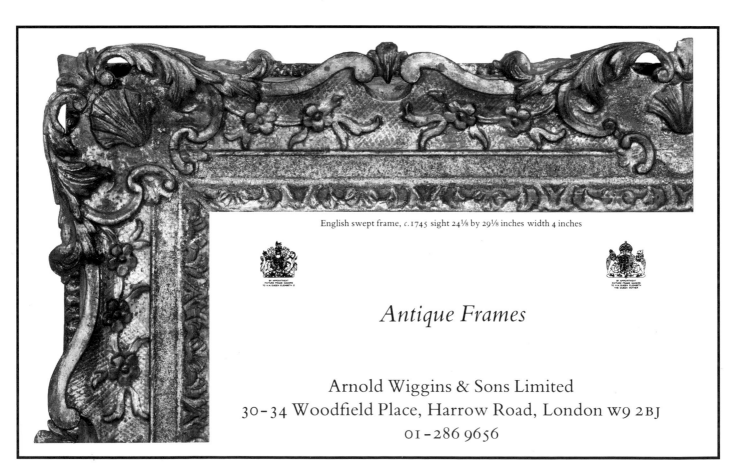

M&D SELIGMANN Antiques

37 Kensington Church Street
London W8 4LL
Telephone 01-937 0400

Very rare oak "Marriage" panelled court cupboard, initialled and dated 1692, cupboard earlier

C. FREDERICKS & SON

EIGHTEENTH-CENTURY
FURNITURE

92 FULHAM ROAD
LONDON SW3 6HR
Telephone: 01-589 5847

*A George II mahogany tea table
with concertina action, circa 1750.*

RICHARD DAVIDSON

— *FINE ANTIQUE FURNITURE* —

0798 42508

A superb Sheraton West Indian satinwood side cabinet, original throughout, 48″ wide, c.1785.

**LOMBARD STREET, PETWORTH
WEST SUSSEX GU28 0AG**

Situated 1 hour
from Central London

LOVIS STANTON

Early Furniture
Works of Art

A fine Charles I oak Wainscot Chair

299-301 Westbourne Grove, London W11
Telephone 01-727 9336

Halsey

Established 1950

Boffins Boft · Bowcombe Creek · Kingsbridge · S. Devon

Showroom Apartment
London SW1 By Private Arrangement

Pimlico, London S.W.1. & Kingsbridge, Devon
Tel. (STD 0548) 2440 24hr Answering Service

Seminars/Tours of Great Houses & Gardens

Courier & Antique Purchasing in
London – Provinces

Interiors & Gardens Created Internationally

17th Century Padouk Chair; Oak Child's Coffer; Gateleg Table; Set of 4 Columns

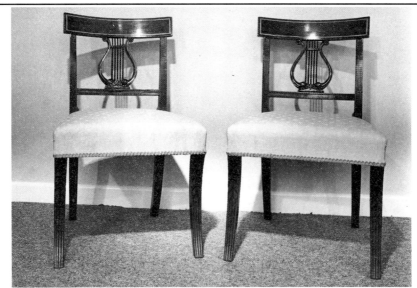

Patrick Sandberg Antiques

Fine English Furniture & Decorative Antiques.

*This Sheraton period figured mahogany
satinwood crossbanded sideboard, circa 1790,
is a typical example of quality period
English furniture available in our
showrooms which are situated in Fulham,
near Parson's Green*

791 Fulham Road, London SW6 5HD. Tel: 01 736 9454.

Peter Brazier

RESTORATION OF PERIOD FURNITURE
(INCLUDING CASTING OF MISSING MOUNTS AND HARDWARE)

Member of

Trade & Private
Commissions

Nash Court Farmhouse
Marnhull
Sturminster Newton
Dorset DT10 1JZ

Regular London
Collections

Tel Marnhull (0258) 820255

In Pursuance of Excellence

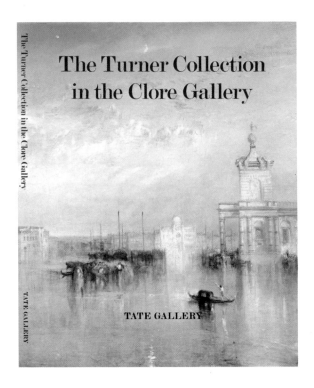

*Restorers of finest English
18th century furniture*

*

*A well established family business
with workshops
in London and Wiltshire*

*

*Antique finding and commission
buying service*

*

A world-wide service

56 Gilstead Road
London SW6
Telephone: 01-736 5329

High Trees House
Savernake Forest
Marlborough
Wiltshire
Tel: Marlborough 53017

VAT No: 311597271

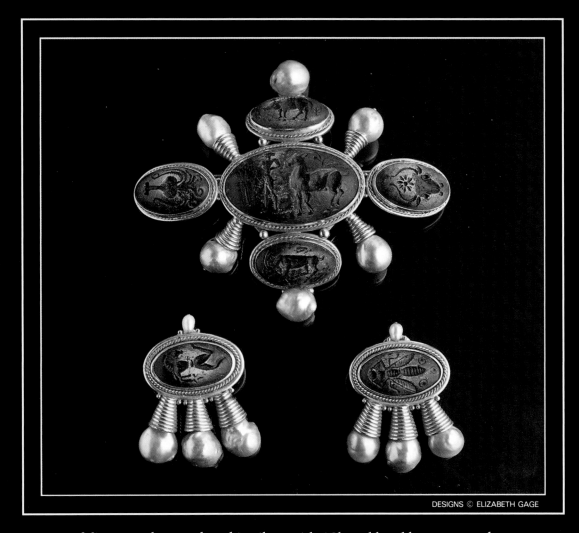

IMPERIAL · TORQUAY

HYDE PARK · LONDON

WALDORF · LONDON

QUEEN'S · CHELTENHAM

The Finest Collection of Hotels in Britain

With nearly 200 hotels around Britain, Trusthouse Forte can offer you a choice everywhere from Plymouth to Pitlochry. But each hotel jealously preserves the individuality which has made it special.

Whether an historic coaching inn deep in English countryside, a grand hotel on Park Lane or a modern airport hotel, Trusthouse Forte hotels have one great virtue in common.

Dedication to the standards of personal service that have made them famous.

Trusthouse Forte Hotels

For reservations telephone: 01-567 3444

The monthly magazine for dealers and collectors.

For subscription rates and a complimentary copy: write to Room 2427, King's Reach Tower, Stamford Street, London SE1 9LS or Telephone 01-261 6894.

OLYMPIA LONDON
5th–14th JUNE 1987
(Closed Monday 8th)

For connoisseurs and browsers alike, the greatest
collection of pre-1930 antiques under
one roof assembled by over 300 established dealers.
Prices from £5–£100,000.

Preview 5th June (2pm–8pm): £12.00.
Midweek (11.30am–8pm) & Weekends (11.30am–6pm): £3.50.
Information: Philbeach Events Ltd., 01-385 1200.

THE BVRLINGTON MAGAZINE

The world's leading magazine for the fine and decorative arts

Muses and Pierides dish, from the workshop of Guido Durantino, Urbino. Fitzwilliam Museum, Cambridge.
See article by John Mallet on Guido Durantino and the Fontana workshop in Urbino,
The Burlington Magazine, May 1987 (**special issue on ceramics**).

UNDER THE PATRONAGE OF HER MAJESTY QUEEN ELIZABETH THE QUEEN MOTHER

THE BURLINGTON HOUSE FAIR

THE ANTIQUE DEALERS' FAIR

at the
Royal Academy of Arts, Piccadilly, London W1
9—20 September 1987.

Leading British and International Dealers will offer for sale Pictures, Furniture and Works of Art all strictly vetted and of the highest quality.

PRESENTED BY ARRANGEMENT WITH THE BURLINGTON MAGAZINE

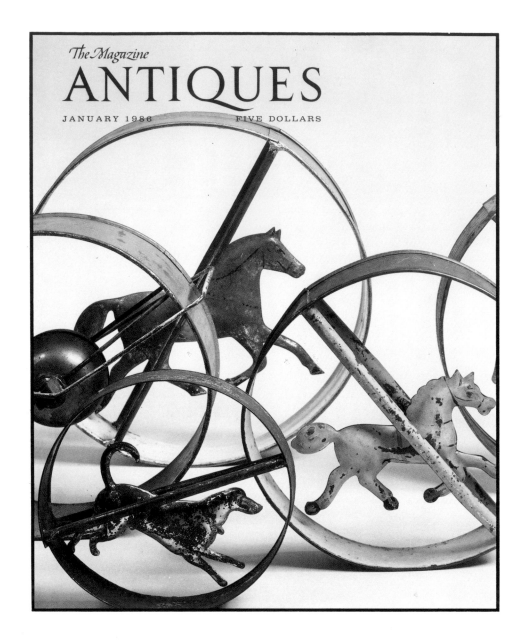

AN AMERICAN CLASSIC

A subscription to *The Magazine* ANTIQUES
is your key to unlocking the richness
of America's past. Its furniture,
architecture, fine and decorative arts,
and one-of-a-kind extraordinary pieces.

To subscribe, write to:
The Magazine ANTIQUES,
Old Mill Road, P.O. Box 1975, Marion Ohio 43305

Harpers & Queen

the clever and influential glossy

*Harpers & Queen is an international magazine for the well-dressed,
the well-read and the well-travelled.
It is also thoroughly British.
Our readers are wholly at their ease in Paris, New York, Milan and the Caribbean,
but have their roots firmly in the British Establishment.
Financially and socially secure, they have the independence
to take a robust interest in the arts, literature and politics.
Harpers & Queen is directed at the whole mind.
We are a magazine for people intelligent enough
to like children, racing, jewellery, oysters and interior decorating;
broadminded enough to be interested in the future of the world.*

HARPERS & QUEEN, 72 BROADWICK STREET, LONDON, W1V 2BP TELEPHONE 01 439 7144

The Antique Collector Awards for the best individual exhibit, and the best stand design and display, have been created by Catherine Hough who specialises in glass. Her work is in several permanent collections including the Varberg Castle Museum, Sweden and the Corning Glass Museum, New York. We commissioned the Awards through Contemporary Applied Arts, London.

Artist's impression of the 1987 Award, height approx. 20 cm, based on a preliminary design by Catherine Hough. The Awards will be presented at a Dinner for the Fair Exhibitors and their guests in the Ballroom of the Grosvenor House on the evening of Tuesday 16th June. The Awards are given in conjunction with the Fair organisers, Evan Steadman and Partners Limited.

THE ANTIQUE
COLLECTOR
AWARDS
for
THE 1987 GROSVENOR
HOUSE ANTIQUES FAIR

THE ANTIQUE
COLLECTOR

**Britain's Largest Circulation
Art and Antiques Magazine**

THE GROSVENOR HOUSE ANTIQUES FAIR

Will be held in 1988 between

8th and 18th June

 In association with The British Antique Dealers' Association

Organised by: Evan Steadman and Partners Limited, The Hub, Emson Close, Saffron Walden, Essex CB10 1HL, England.
Telephone: (0799) 26699. Telex: 81653 INFORM G. Fax: (0799) 26088.
For further details of the 1988 Fair and how to purchase its Handbook, please contact the Organisers.

43589